Carpentry and Joinery   1

R. BAYLISS F.B.I.C.C., F.I.M.Wood T.
Formerly Lecturer at Walsall Technical College, Norwich
City College and Art School and Mid-Essex Technical College
and School of Art, Chelmsford.

Carpentry and Joinery | 1

Stanley Thornes (Publishers) Ltd

Originally published in 1961 by Hutchinson Education
Revised and metricated 1969
Reprinted 1970, 1971, 1973, 1975, 1976, 1978, 1980, 1981, 1982, 1985 and 1987

Reprinted in 1990 by
Stanley Thornes (Publishers) Ltd
Old Station Drive
Leckhampton
CHELTENHAM GL53 0DN

Reprinted 1992

ISBN 0 7487 0292 X

Printed in Great Britain
by Scotprint Ltd, Musselburgh.

Contents

Preface

This book is the first of four volumes planned to cover the theory and practice of the Carpentry and Joinery and Machine Woodworking Courses of the City and Guilds of London Institute and other examining institutions.

The author's approach and presentation is essentially visual; the text serving largely as an explanation and extension of the diagrams. The amount of subject matter in each volume more than covers the requirements of the C.G.L.I. syllabus, and provides the reader with an introduction to the next stage.

An introduction to the change to metric is given in chapter 1, and practice lessons directly related to the subject matter in the book are given at the end of each main chapter.

The work has a strong practical bias, with emphasis on method, and is intended mainly to assist the apprentices and craftsmen with limited practical experience.

The author hopes that the books will stimulate individual study, and enable all those engaged in the woodworking branches of the building industry to gain valuable information in addition to that acquired by attendance at educational institutions.

R BAYLISS

It is the popular view that the change to the metric system of measurement will give the construction industries a unique opportunity to reconsider the dimensions we have commonly used in buildings and for building components.

It is important that we have ranges of components—such as doors and frames, windows, or curtain walling—that are dimensionally co-ordinated.

A building could be designed around a wide range of standardised components, thus limiting the need for non-standard units, or for the site trimming of units.

It is essential that building craftsmen become rapidly accustomed to working in metric sizes—millimetres, centimetres, metres—and visualise their relative size as against the imperial $\frac{1}{16}$ *in*–$\frac{1}{4}$ *in*, $\frac{1}{2}$ *in*–1 *inch* and the *foot*.

A diagram illustrating the relative difference between *imperial* and *metric* units of measure is given on page 4.

The metric rule is graduated to measure in millimetres, and the yard (or 3 ft rule) to measure in feet and inches.

Notice that 300 mm on the metric rule is approximately equal to 1 ft (305 mm) on the imperial rule; 200 mm is equal to 8 in (203 mm); 100 mm is equal to 4 in (101 mm); 50 mm equal to 2 in (50 mm) and 25 mm equal to 1 in (25 mm).

These five dimensions (300–200–100–50–25 mm) are the recommended first basic sizes for co-ordinating the dimensions of component parts.

From the illustrations on page 4 it will be seen that a square metre contains 10·76 square feet; a cubic metre 35·31 cubic feet; a square yard 9 square feet; and a cubic yard 27 cubic feet.

It is advisable, therefore, to study the diagrams carefully in order to visualise, and memorise, one millimetre, 100 millimetres, 300 millimetres, and the metre as units of square and cubic measure.

Use of planning grid

A planning grid is a series of lines set out in squares, the intervals of which are based upon multiples of a module, or increment of size. The British Standards Institution recommend 300 millimetres as the first preference and 100 millimetres as a second preference. The lines of the planning grid will control the overall dimensions of the structure, also the location, and size, of the components.

The use of a 300 mm planning grid is illustrated on page 5. The door opening is shown at a standard width of 900 mm and the windows correspond with the grid lines.

An enlarged view of one square, of a 300 mm planning grid, is shown on page 6, and details of door and window openings to suit the grid are given at the foot of the page.

It will be seen that if the overall width of the frame is standard, in this case 900 mm, any variation in the thickness of the framing will give varying door sizes. 50 mm framing will give an 850 mm (2 ft 9½ in imperial measure) door width, and 75 mm framing will give an 800 mm (2 ft 7½ in imperial measure) door width.

Metric height of rooms

The building regulations state that the minimum height of rooms shall not be less than 7 ft 6 in, giving a floor to floor height of approximately 8·2 ft.

The room, and floor to floor, heights, in metric and imperial measure, are given on page 7.

The five room heights are shown set out on the 300 mm planning grid.

Metric sizes of timber

Commencing in the year 1970 softwoods will be imported into the country in a new range of sizes in metric measurement. The section sizes are given in millimetres, and the lengths in metres.

These new sizes are slightly under the corresponding imperial sizes. This is due to the fact that 12 in is taken to equal 300 mm (11·8 in).

The chart below illustrates this:

Section sizes

Imperial measure (inches)	1 × 3	2 × 4	3 × 6	4 × 12
Metric measure (mm)	25 × 75	50 × 100	75 × 150	100 × 300

Lengths

Imperial measure (feet)	8	9	10	15	20
Metric measure (metres)	2·40	2·70	3·00	4·50	6·00

CARPENTRY AND JOINERY.

METRICATION
INTRODUCTION

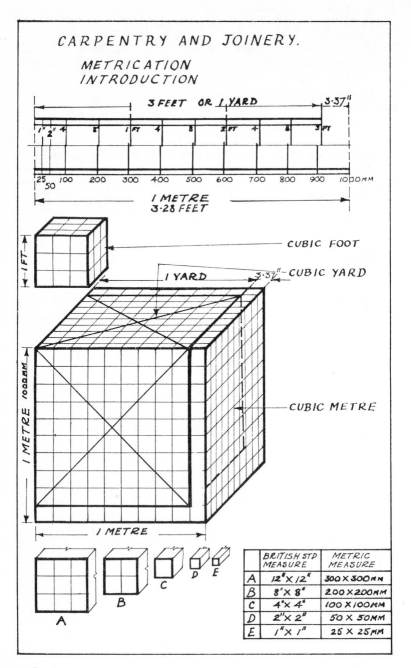

	BRITISH STD MEASURE	METRIC MEASURE
A	12" × 12"	300 × 300 mm
B	8" × 8"	200 × 200 mm
C	4" × 4"	100 × 100 mm
D	2" × 2"	50 × 50 mm
E	1" × 1"	25 × 25 mm

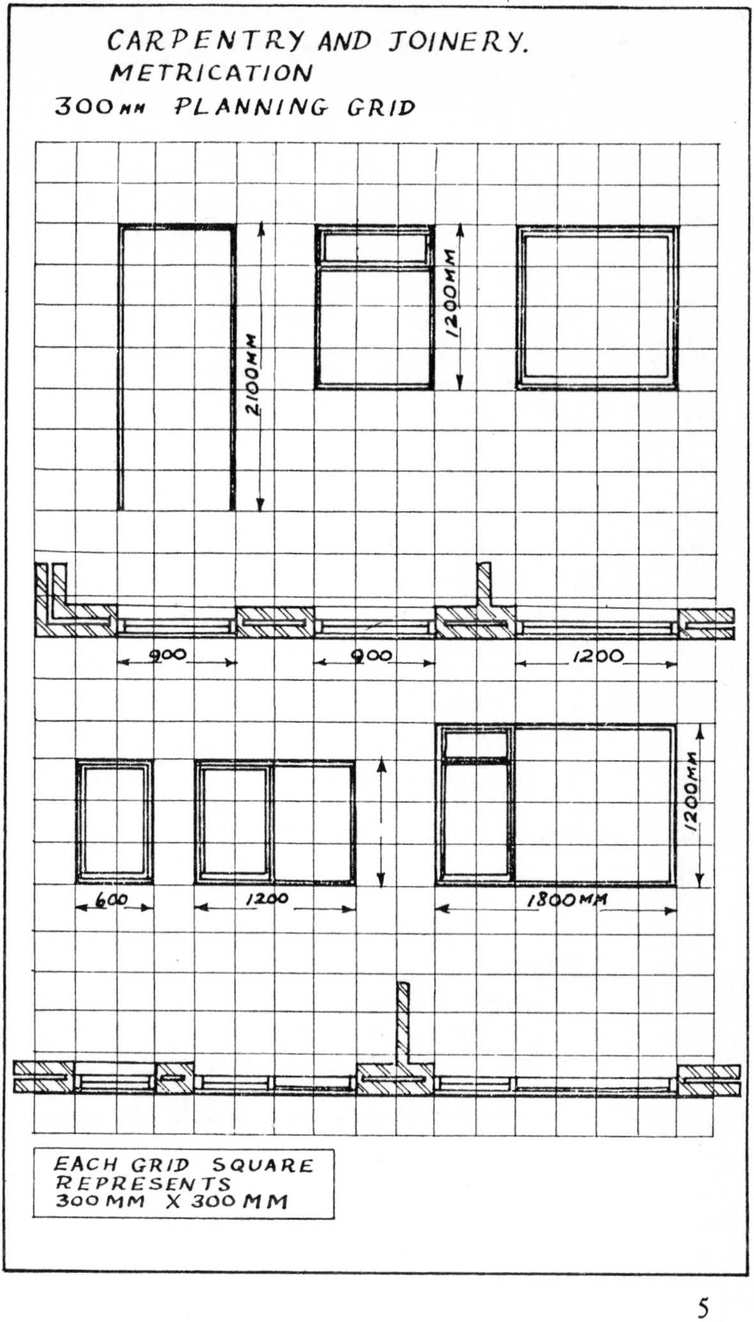

CARPENTRY AND JOINERY.
METRICATION
300ₘₘ PLANNING GRID

2100MM

1200MM

900

900

1200

1200MM

600

1200

1800MM

EACH GRID SQUARE
REPRESENTS
300 MM X 300 MM

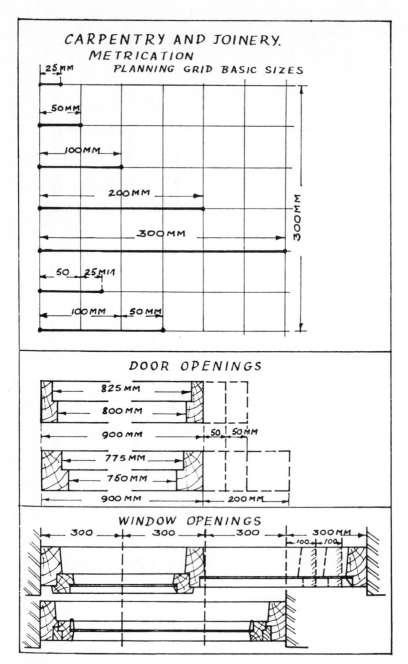

CARPENTRY AND JOINERY.
METRICATION
PLANNING GRID BASIC SIZES

25 MM

50 MM

100 MM

200 MM

300 MM

50 25 MM

100 MM   50 MM

300 MM

DOOR OPENINGS

825 MM

800 MM

900 MM   50 | 50 MM

775 MM

750 MM

900 MM   200 MM

WINDOW OPENINGS

300   300   300   300 MM

100 | 100

6

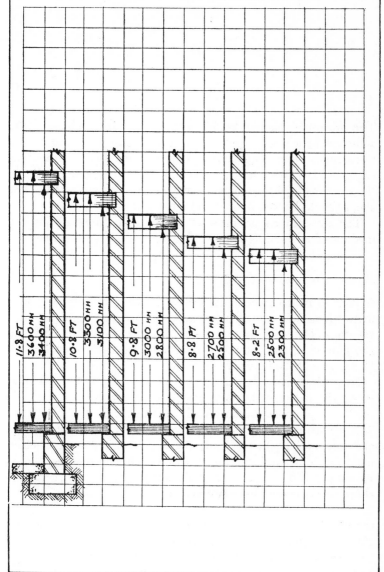

CARPENTRY AND JOINERY.
METRICATION

METRIC STOREY HEIGHTS

11·8 FT 3600 MM 3400 MM

10·8 FT 3300 MM 3100 MM

9·8 FT 3000 MM 2800 MM

8·8 FT 2700 MM 2500 MM

8·2 FT 2500 MM 2300 MM

7

2 | Workshops

The workshop should be big enough to give each workman sufficient bench room plus the space required to assemble his work. Since a high proportion of joiners' shops are mechanised the larger ones will have separate assembly and machine shops, but in the smaller shops the machines may be grouped at one end. The shops should be well lighted and adequately heated.

The illustrations on page 11 show a typical small shop, a medium-sized building contractor's shop, and a large joinery works.

Benches and equipment

A joiner's bench popular in Britain is the double type, 3 to 4 metres long, 900 mm wide, and 750 to 950 mm high (see page 12—top). The working tops should be at least 75 mm thick and 280 mm wide, and should preferably be made of beech, though European redwood gives years of satisfactory service.

Each bench is equipped with a vice and a stop. The instantaneous vice has many advantages over the screw type. The well in the bench provides space for tools in frequent use.

It is essential that apprentices develop at an early age methodical and tidy working habits. Only the tools required for the job in hand should be on the bench, and all tools in constant use should have their allotted place. The illustration on page 12 (middle) shows a layout used by many joiners.

NOTE Planes are put at the head of the bench with the mallet and chisels next to them, and the measuring, testing and sharpening tools are in the centre of the bench. Notice also that the tools for each workman occupy one half of the bench only.

In addition to the metal equipment used in the shop, most joiners make many pieces of wooden equipment for themselves:

1 A bench hook for shoulder cutting and squaring off.

2 A bench peg for supporting long boards (notice the holes on the bench side which make it possible for the peg to be put into varying positions).

3 A mitre block for cutting small mouldings and beads.

4 A mitre box for cutting architraves, cornice and bed mouldings.

These pieces of equipment are illustrated on page 12 (foot).

Useful hints

1 The bench must be kept clean and tidy if good work is to be produced.

2 Only those tools in constant use need be on the bench.

3 Tools should always be put back in their proper places after being used.

4 The bench way must be kept clean.

5 All waste, tenon cheeks and short ends should be put at once into the cuttings bin. This will keep the floor clear and thus prevent accidents.

6 Convenient storage space must be provided for all bench equipment.

Shop equipment

Every joiner needs one or two sawing stools for his own use. Benches should be sturdily built but light in weight, with a height usually of 450 to 500 mm, legs 50 × 75 mm, and a top 75 × 100 mm. The illustration on page 13 (top) shows a popular design.

The number of cramps needed will depend on the class and size of the work in hand. Every joiner must have at least one sash cramp for setting out and for the assembly of small pieces of work. The cramps used in most shops vary in length from 1 to 2 m, and have extension bars to give extra length when necessary. Joiners often make wooden cleats which they use when assembling and jointing up boards. Gee cramps are extensively used for holding small members together when glueing or working.

Two types of wooden cleats and metal cramps in common use are illustrated on page 13 (foot).

Timber storage and tool maintenance

In addition to the actual workshops, storage under cover should be provided for timber. Large works will also require seasoning kilns, and separate accommodation for machine tool maintenance and storage. In the tool room, band and circular saws are maintained in working condition, rotary cutters are profiled, and set up on the cutting heads for use on planers, spindle moulders and four siders. Accommodation should be provided for the finishing of woodwork, for painting, polishing and treating it with preservative. High-class joinery work must be stored when finished in an air-conditioned warehouse or dispatch department.

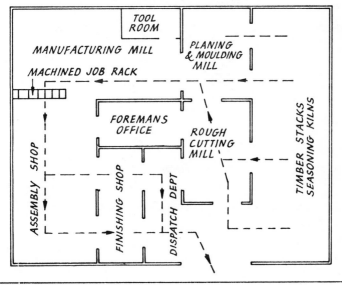

SMALL WORKSHOP

TIMBER STORE   MACHINE   BENCHES   OFFICE   STORES

MEDIUM SIZE WORKSHOP

FOREMANS OFFICE   TOOLS   MACHINE SHOP

JOINERS SHOP   FINISHING SHOP   DISPATCH   TIMBER STACKS

LARGE JOINERY WORKS

TOOL ROOM

MANUFACTURING MILL   PLANING & MOULDING MILL

MACHINED JOB RACK

FOREMANS OFFICE   ROUGH CUTTING MILL

ASSEMBLY SHOP   FINISHING SHOP   DISPATCH DEPT   TIMBER STACKS SEASONING KILNS

WORK BENCH

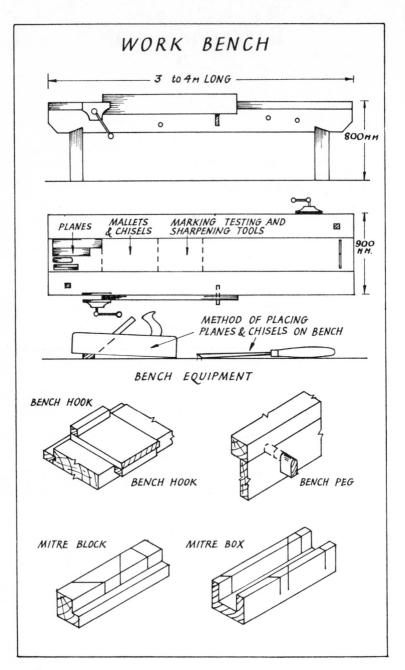

3 to 4 M LONG

800 MM

PLANES   MALLETS   MARKING TESTING AND
          & CHISELS SHARPENING TOOLS

900 MM.

METHOD OF PLACING
PLANES & CHISELS ON BENCH

BENCH EQUIPMENT

BENCH HOOK

BENCH HOOK

BENCH PEG

MITRE BLOCK   MITRE BOX

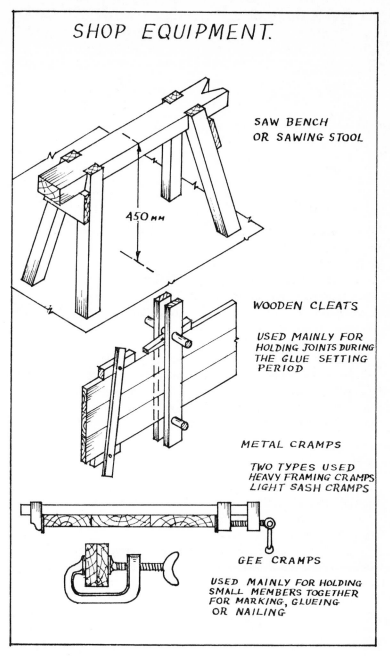

SHOP EQUIPMENT.

SAW BENCH
OR SAWING STOOL

450 MM

WOODEN CLEATS

USED MAINLY FOR
HOLDING JOINTS DURING
THE GLUE SETTING
PERIOD

METAL CRAMPS

TWO TYPES USED
HEAVY FRAMING CRAMPS
LIGHT SASH CRAMPS

GEE CRAMPS

USED MAINLY FOR HOLDING
SMALL MEMBERS TOGETHER
FOR MARKING, GLUEING
OR NAILING

Classification of hand tools

Woodworking hand tools can best be classified in the following main groups:

(a)   Parting and shearing tools (saws)
(b)   Slicing and smoothing tools (planes)
(c)   Shaping tools (chisels, gouges)
(d)   Measuring, marking, and testing tools (rules, gauges, try squares, bevels, plumb rules, etc.)
(e)   Fixing tools (hammers, screwdrivers, nail punches, etc.)
(f)   Boring tools (twist drills, drills, bradawls, etc.).

Many of the tools have been designed for a specific purpose. For example, the trying plane was specially designed to produce large, flat surfaces and long, straight edge joints; the bull-nose for working into corners; and the spoke-shave for shaped work.

The action of woodworking tools

Woodworking tools employ one of two types of action: they cut or they abrade. Cutting is done with axes, chisels, gouges, planes, draw-knives, boring bits and saws; abrading with toothing planes, scrapers, files and glass paper.

Wood *chisels* are bevelled on one side only. The chisel has a paring action which removes thin layers of wood. This paring action, both with and across the grain, is shown on page 24 (top).

A *plane iron* consists merely of a chisel, to which a back iron is attached, fixed securely in a wood or metal plane in order to remove a shaving of uniform thickness. The size of the plane mouth considerably affects the standard of the surface finish.

There is nothing to stop the cutter on a wide-mouthed plane from splitting the wood; the mouth should be just wide enough to allow the shaving to pass through (page 24—middle). The cutting iron is usually held in the plane at an angle of 45°; this is slightly less in special planes designed for working difficult hardwoods. Special planes designed to work end grain (shoulder planes and block planes) have single cutting irons pitched at an angle of 30° or less. The iron is placed face down in the plane, with a grinding bevel acting as a back iron (see page 24—middle).

The *saw*'s cutting action may be designed either for slitting or cross-cutting. The slitting action is called 'ripping', and for this purpose saws have large teeth (four to 25 mm) with very little set. Cross-cutting demands a saw with needle-shaped teeth in order that the grain should be severed, and a clean cut made. The teeth are much smaller than those of a ripping saw, and are set six or eight to 25 mm; also, the cutting angle is more acute. Clearance of the saw blade is provided for by bending each tooth over alternately to the right and left of the blade. This is called 'setting'. The amount of clearance should be just enough to enable the saw to work freely. For clean, efficient cutting it is essential that all teeth should be in perfect line, that each tooth should be the same size and shape, and have exactly the same amount of set to each side. Both types of saw teeth are illustrated at the foot of page 24.

CUTTING TOOLS: *(a)* SAWS

Rip saws

The *full rip saw* is 750 mm long, and has three teeth to 25 mm. It is not much used nowadays since its work is now largely mechanised, but it was designed for converting or ripping timber into suitable smaller sections. This and the following saws are shown on page 25.

The *half rip saw* is extensively used in small hand shops for tenon ripping and ripping out material.

Cross-cutting saws

The *hand saw* has a stout blade 500 to 650 mm long, with six to eight teeth to 25 mm.

The *panel saw* is used for fine cutting. It is 450 to 500 mm long, with eight to ten teeth to 25 mm.

The *tenon saw* or *backed saw* has a stiffened blade with a solid metal back. One of its chief uses is for cutting shoulders, and it would be more accurately termed a shoulder saw. Its length varies from 300 to 450 mm, and the most popular length among joiners is the 350 mm.

The *dovetail saw* is a smaller type of back saw, from 150 to 200 mm long, with twelve to sixteen teeth to 25 mm.

Materials used in the manufacture of saws

High-quality steel for the making of saw blades is produced in large quantities in America, Britain, and Sweden, and all three countries make excellent saws. The manufacturing processes are extremely specialised. Much thought has been given to the shape of the handle, blade and saw teeth, and steels have been specially developed to the right degree of hardness and toughness. Tensioning, too, is a highly skilled process.

The result is that saws are comfortable to use, and will stand up to hard cutting in difficult timbers for long periods. This applies particularly to saws made in Sweden from charcoal steel.

Sharpening of saws

Study of one of the handbooks issued by the saw manufacturers, followed by sufficient practice, is the sure way of acquiring skill in saw sharpening. Each tooth should be the right shape, the set must be uniform, and the points of the teeth in line. The sequence of operations for sharpening a saw is as follows:

(a) The saw must be firmly fixed in the clamp.

(b) The points of the teeth must be put in alignment with a flat file.

(c) The teeth must be set with a spring saw set, and they should be gripped only at the points in order to prevent them from breaking. This applies particularly to saws of Swedish make.

(d) The filing should be done with a saw file which is the right size for the saw teeth, and with the saw kept level so that the teeth remain the same size. A common fault among beginners and

apprentices is to pitch the file upwards. This soon produces uneven teeth.

(e) Very often, in order to produce a fine cut, the teeth are side-dressed with a stone.

CUTTING TOOLS: *(b)* PLANES

Three main planes are used on the bench (see page 26). These are the jack plane, trying plane and smoothing plane. All three have the same kind of cutting unit, which consists of a cutting iron, back iron and wedge. It is an advantage to have all cutting irons the same width, since they are then interchangeable.

The *jack plane* is used mainly for the removal of waste and for all rough planing. Its length of 380 mm enables one to straight-plane satisfactorily.

The *trying plane* is the largest plane a joiner uses. It is for straight-planing and levelling, and its length varies from 560 to 600 mm. The 600 mm type is used mainly for joint shooting.

The *smoothing plane* is the finishing plane, and is also used for working end grain. This plane is still in constant use, whereas the jack plane and trying plane are now going out because joiners use much more machined wood than they did in the past.

Designs and materials used in planes

Planes are made both in wood (beech) and metal, though the metal plane is gradually replacing the wooden type for many classes of work. The cutting units are of similar design in both wood and metal varieties, and both planes are illustrated on page 26 (foot).

As with saw blades, steels have been developed which have the right quality of toughness for the plane irons, but are yet soft enough to be sharpened by the ordinary equipment (grindstones and oilstones). Plane irons for wooden planes usually have a facing of tough steel. The rest of the iron, being of softer steel, can easily be ground.

The grinding and sharpening of plane irons

If the iron is set in the plane at an angle of 45° and the grinding angle is 30°, the clearance angle will be 15°. The sharpening angle will, however, reduce this clearance angle to between 5° and 8° (see page 27).

Grinding may be done on a sandstone or a carborundum wheel; but when the latter is used great care must be taken to prevent the steel from burning.

The natural oil-stones, of which the washita was the most used, have now been replaced by manufactured varieties—the India and carborundum stones. Natural stones are not uniform in structure and require frequent rubbing down when in constant use. India stones, however, are popular with many joiners, since they are uniform in structure and will remain flat and level after many years of use. The stones are often made in two parts, one fine and the other coarse. The size in common use is 200 × 50 mm.

The angle at which the iron is held on the stone when being sharpened is very important. It should not be more than 40°, giving a clearance angle of 5°; any higher degree will give a clearance angle of nil. By holding the hand over the plane iron when sharpening it, the risk of reducing the clearance angle to nil is eliminated.

The ideal plane finish is flat, and this can only be achieved with a cutting iron that is straight, on its edge, and with its corners taken off to prevent ridging.

Trying and smoothing planes need straight cutting edges. The jack plane iron, however, often has a round cutting edge so that it will work easily. These points are illustrated on page 27 (foot).

CUTTING TOOLS: *(c)* CHISELS

Chisels are classified according to their use. They are shown on page 28.

Firmer chisels are the jack planes of the chisels. They may be used for light mortising, chopping out, paring, and all work for which a chisel is required. They are obtainable in widths from 3 to 50 mm.

Mortise chisels are stouter than firmer chisels so that they can withstand the heavy mallet blows and levering necessary when the joiner is making large and deep mortises. They are obtainable in widths from 2 to 25 mm.

Bevelled edge chisels are bevelled on each side, and are thus ideal for dovetailing and working into corners. They are obtainable in sizes from 3 to 50 mm.

Paring chisels are, in fact, long bevelled-edge chisels, and are used for cleaning deep mortises, stop chamfering, and so on. The joiner normally has only one paring chisel, 25 or 35 mm wide.

Grinding and sharpening chisels

As with plane irons, it is wise to follow the instructions of the manufacturer for grinding and sharpening angles. A chisel that is too thick will only punch away the timber, and a chisel that is too thin will easily break off at the point.

For soft, easy working timbers a long bevel is most suitable, whereas for hard, difficult timbers a thicker grinding angle is necessary, as is shown in the illustrations on page 28 (foot).

CUTTING TOOLS: *(d)* GOUGES

Gouges may be defined as curved chisels, and are mainly used for shaping, carving, and scribing. They are ground on the inside for scribing and on the outside for shaping and carving. They are shown on page 28 (middle).

Grinding and sharpening of gouges

The grinding of gouges is usually carried out on a grinding wheel. For inside ground gouges, a wheel profiled to the shape of the gouge is used, but for outside ground gouges a flat wheel is needed.

Finger slip stones are necessary for the purpose. These have two curved edges to suit all sizes of gouge, as is shown in the illustration on page 28 (foot).

MEASURING, MARKING, AND TESTING TOOLS

Measuring tools must be accurate, and like cutting tools they must be kept in good condition. The points of the gauge's two pins should always be kept sharp, and the locking screw in good order. Try squares should be checked periodically to make sure that all the right angles are true. The tools are illustrated on page 29.

Metric-imperial folding rules, with steel spring joints, will be extensively used by carpenters and joiners during the transitional period of change to the metric system. The rules are of the ten and six fold type, and are available in two sizes, one metre and two metres long.

The two metre rule is most convenient for the carpenter and joiner.

Steel rules and steel tapes are used for the accurate measurement of greater lengths.

It is common practice for the carpenter or joiner to make *measuring rods* in wood for use on a particular job. These are usually made of 20 × 40 mm lath, and are marked off in metres and 100 mm.

The *try square* is a templet for drawing right angles, and consists of a stock and blade. When in use, the stock will act as a fence, and the blade as a guide for marking the angle. The sizes most favoured by joiners are the 100 mm, 150 mm, and 300 mm. These measurements refer to the blade sizes.

In addition to these, larger wooden *squares* are made by the carpenter for the setting out of large structural work. The squares should be made in hardwood (mahogany), and great care must be taken in their manufacture.

The *sliding bevel* is in fact an adjustable square for marking angles between 0° and 180°. It consists of a stock and sliding blade, with a screw or wing nut, as is shown on page 29. The sizes in common use are the 100 mm, 150 mm, 200 mm, and 250 mm.

The *pencil* is a most important part of a joiner's equipment, and it is advisable to have the correct grade for the job in hand. Gradings of H, 3H and F are all popular for marking dimensions and joints. For face marks and other instructions a dark, easy to read line is needed, and for this work HB grade is the most suitable. Pencil crayons may also be used.

Pencils can be sharpened to an ordinary point or to a chisel point. Most craftsmen use a chisel point for marking joints and an ordinary point for face marks and written instructions.

NOTE   It is advisable not to use a blue copying pencil, as the mark cannot be removed and will show through paintwork, stain or polish.

Marking knives are used mainly for marking shoulders and any other marking out where great accuracy is necessary. The knife has a slanting chisel edge. Care should be taken when marking joints with these tools, since at least 1 mm of timber would have to be removed in order to plane out a knife mark made by mistake.

A marking knife as bought from a tool merchant has a chisel point at one end and a scribing point at the other; but a great many joiners prefer to use one made from an old table knife by shaping and sharpening its blade.

Gauges may be classified according to the number of pins in the gauge or the purpose for which it is used. The ordinary marking gauge is also known as a single pin or tooth gauge. It is essential for accurate working that the head should slide easily on the stem, that the pins should be sharp, and, in the case of the mortise gauge, that these should be of an equal length. They are shown on page 29. Gauges can be made of box, beech, rosewood or ebony.

A *cutting gauge* is a single tooth gauge with a knife-shaped cutter instead of a pin. It is used mainly for cutting in small quirks, but is also good for cutting across the grain. The cutter is usually held in position by a wedge.

Pencil compasses for drawing small circles 25 to 300 mm in diameter are essential in the joiner's shop. For larger curves a beam compass, with trammel heads, is the most convenient tool to use. The beam, generally made of ash, can be made to a maximum length of 1·5 metres. The trammel heads have steel points, and one head should have a pencil socket.

Scribing compasses, which have steel points, are used when one member needs shaping to fit another; for example, when skirtings have to be scribed to fit floors.

FIXING TOOLS

A list of fixing tools includes those for measuring and testing, together with other tools which drive in the fixing members.

Plumb rules, straight edges, spirit levels, and squaring rods are all testing tools. In the second group there are hammers, mallets, screwdrivers, pincers, steel chisels, plugging chisels, wall drills, and nail punches. They are illustrated on page 30.

Two types of *plumb rules* are used: first, a level and plumb rule combined, and second, a plumb rule only (usually made by the joiner himself). The plumb rule is about 1·4 metres long, and is very handy for fixing joinery, door casings, linings, and screens. The combined plumb rule and level, though shorter in length, can be used for all kinds of plumbing and levelling work on floors and roofs. Both types are illustrated on page 30 (middle).

Levelling can be accurately carried out with the help of a small *spirit level*. A straight edge, usually 2 to 3 metres long, is also needed. The levels are 230 to 300 mm long, and the straight edges must be accurately made from sound, straight-grained timber (see page 30—middle).

Two main types of *hammer* are in use today; the pane or Warrington type and the claw hammer. The Warrington hammer is usually used in the shop, and the claw hammer for outside fixing.

The handles of these tools are made in ash or hickory, though a steel and rubber-shafted claw hammer has been developed in Sweden.

The head of the *mallet* needs frequent replacement because of the kind of work this tool is called upon to do. Suitable materials for the head are beech, box and, in the case of heavy mallets, lignum vitae.

Three types of *screwdriver* are well known in the woodworking trades:

1   The ordinary screwdriver, which is made in various sizes. The joiner usually manages with one small and one large size.

2   The *ratchet screwdriver*, which is not popular, is used for small screws only.

3   The *spiral* or *pump screwdriver*. This has many advantages over the other two, and has come into general use for all kinds of fixing work. The latest development has been the introduction of interchangeable bits, drills and counter sinks, which enable the joiner to carry out all the operations connected with inserting the screw using one tool only.

If the screwdriver is to be properly maintained, it is essential that its end should fit the nick in the head of the screw properly. The correct shape for the end of the screwdriver is shown on page 30.

Bradawls are used chiefly to form holes before inserting small screws and nails. They may also be used as screwdrivers to insert small screws.

Nail punches vary in size from small pin punches with a point, to large punches 10 mm wide. Small punches are apt to slip, and care must be taken to prevent this from happening.

Cold chisels and *plugging chisels* are gradually being replaced by portable power drills, but they are still necessary for small work. The steel chisels are used for cutting out openings in brickwork to receive structural members, and plugging chisels for raking out the joints between bricks in order to receive wooden plugs.

BORING TOOLS

Most boring and drilling is now done with portable power tools. The cutting tools used are, in principle, the same as the equivalent hand tools. The various types are illustrated on page 31.

Bits and drills

The standard *twist bit* of the Jennings pattern is used extensively for general boring work; a shorter one is made specifically for dowelling.

A *centre bit*, a very old design, is most suitable for boring clean holes in thin material. This bit has no thread on the point, and requires pressure when one is boring end grain.

Bits are fitted into a brace, the handle of which revolves on a 125 mm sweep. Sometimes it is necessary to bore holes in or near corners, and in order to do this a ratchet is used on the brace.

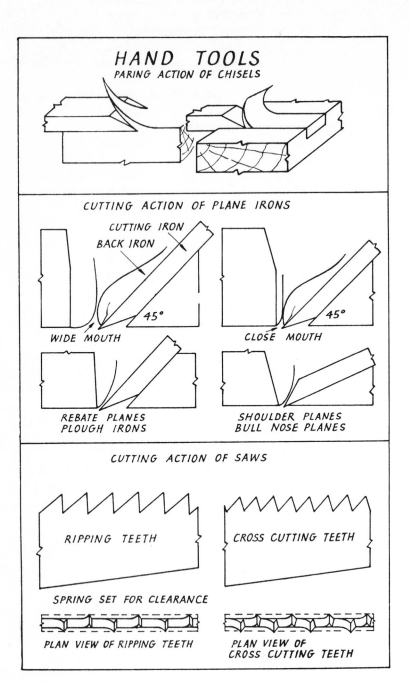

HAND TOOLS
PARING ACTION OF CHISELS

CUTTING ACTION OF PLANE IRONS

CUTTING IRON

BACK IRON

45°

WIDE MOUTH

CLOSE MOUTH

REBATE PLANES
PLOUGH IRONS

SHOULDER PLANES
BULL NOSE PLANES

CUTTING ACTION OF SAWS

RIPPING TEETH

CROSS CUTTING TEETH

SPRING SET FOR CLEARANCE

PLAN VIEW OF RIPPING TEETH

PLAN VIEW OF
CROSS CUTTING TEETH

24

CUTTING TOOLS
SAWS

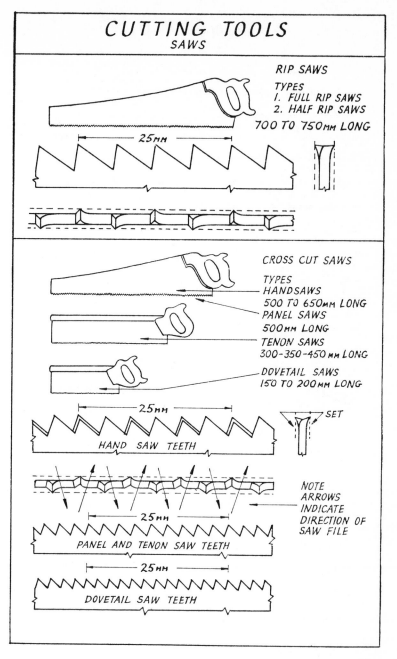

RIP SAWS

TYPES
1. FULL RIP SAWS
2. HALF RIP SAWS

700 TO 750mm LONG

25mm

CROSS CUT SAWS

TYPES
HANDSAWS
500 TO 650mm LONG
PANEL SAWS
500mm LONG
TENON SAWS
300-350-450 mm LONG

DOVETAIL SAWS
150 TO 200mm LONG

25mm

SET

HAND SAW TEETH

NOTE
ARROWS
INDICATE
DIRECTION OF
SAW FILE

25mm

PANEL AND TENON SAW TEETH

25mm

DOVETAIL SAW TEETH

CUTTING TOOLS
PLANES

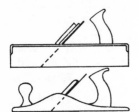

JACK PLANES

WOODEN 380mm LONG
56mm CUTTING IRON

METAL 380mm LONG
50+62mm CUTTING IRON

TRYING PLANES

WOODEN 560mm LONG
60mm CUTTING IRON

METAL 560mm LONG
60mm CUTTING IRON

SMOOTHING PLANES

WOODEN 200mm LONG
55mm CUTTING IRON

METAL 250mm LONG
50 + 62mm CUTTING IRON

CUTTING IRONS

WOODEN PLANES
CUTTING IRON
BACK IRON

METAL PLANES
CUTTING IRON
BACK IRON

47°

47°

THICK CUTTING IRON
HAMMER ADJUSTMENT

THIN CUTTING IRON
SCREW ADJUSTMENT

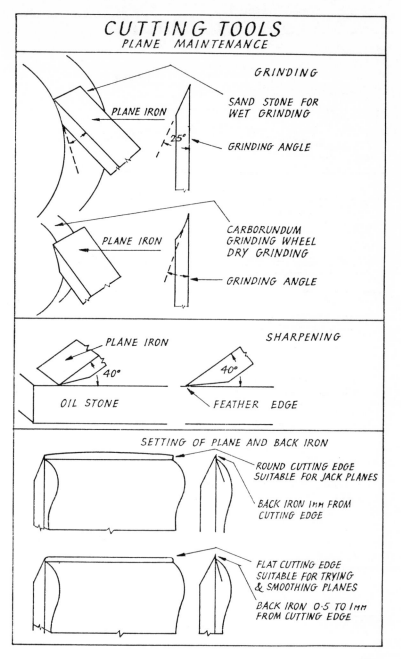

CUTTING TOOLS
PLANE MAINTENANCE

GRINDING

PLANE IRON

SAND STONE FOR
WET GRINDING

25°   GRINDING ANGLE

PLANE IRON

CARBORUNDUM
GRINDING WHEEL
DRY GRINDING

GRINDING ANGLE

SHARPENING

PLANE IRON

40°

40°

OIL STONE

FEATHER EDGE

SETTING OF PLANE AND BACK IRON

ROUND CUTTING EDGE
SUITABLE FOR JACK PLANES

BACK IRON 1mm FROM
CUTTING EDGE

FLAT CUTTING EDGE
SUITABLE FOR TRYING
& SMOOTHING PLANES

BACK IRON 0·5 TO 1mm
FROM CUTTING EDGE

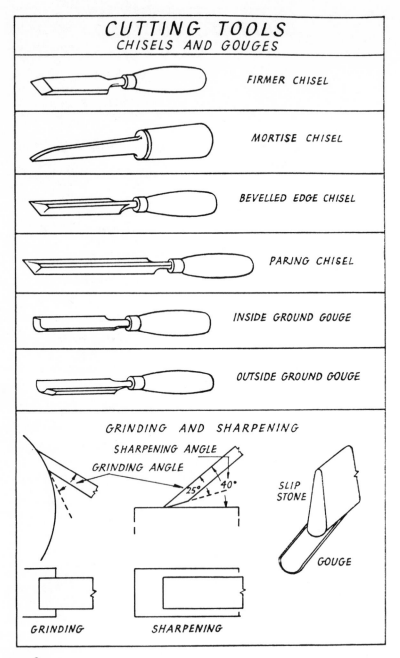

CUTTING TOOLS
CHISELS AND GOUGES

FIRMER CHISEL

MORTISE CHISEL

BEVELLED EDGE CHISEL

PARING CHISEL

INSIDE GROUND GOUGE

OUTSIDE GROUND GOUGE

GRINDING AND SHARPENING

SHARPENING ANGLE

GRINDING ANGLE

25°   40°

SLIP STONE

GOUGE

GRINDING   SHARPENING

MEASURING, MARKING & TESTING TOOLS

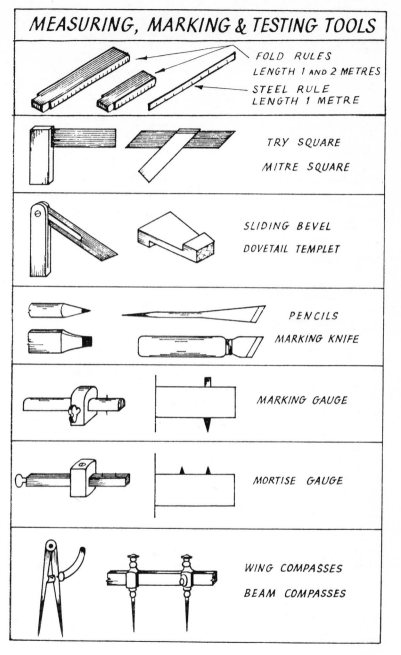

FOLD RULES
LENGTH 1 AND 2 METRES

STEEL RULE
LENGTH 1 METRE

TRY SQUARE

MITRE SQUARE

SLIDING BEVEL

DOVETAIL TEMPLET

PENCILS

MARKING KNIFE

MARKING GAUGE

MORTISE GAUGE

WING COMPASSES

BEAM COMPASSES

FIXING TOOLS

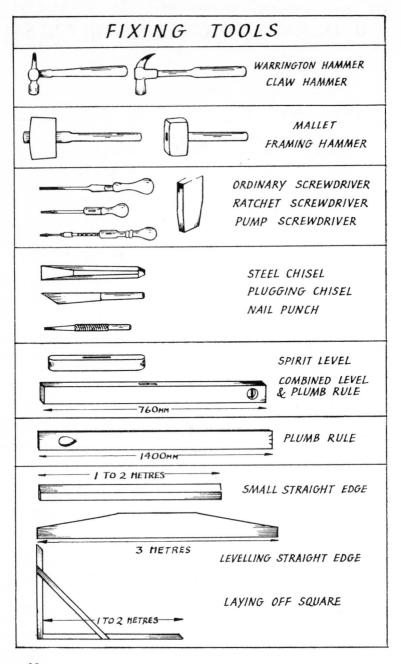

WARRINGTON HAMMER
CLAW HAMMER

MALLET
FRAMING HAMMER

ORDINARY SCREWDRIVER
RATCHET SCREWDRIVER
PUMP SCREWDRIVER

STEEL CHISEL
PLUGGING CHISEL
NAIL PUNCH

SPIRIT LEVEL
COMBINED LEVEL
& PLUMB RULE

760MM

PLUMB RULE

1400MM

1 TO 2 METRES

SMALL STRAIGHT EDGE

3 METRES

LEVELLING STRAIGHT EDGE

LAYING OFF SQUARE

1 TO 2 METRES

BORING TOOLS

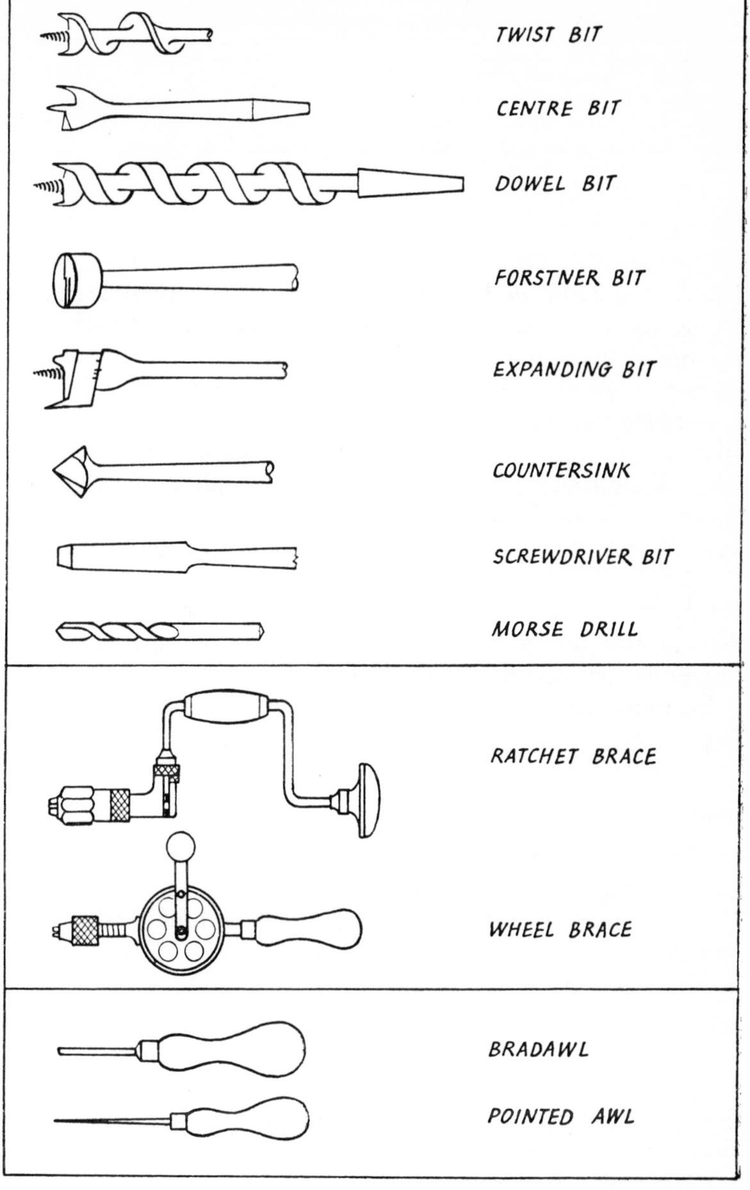

TWIST BIT

CENTRE BIT

DOWEL BIT

FORSTNER BIT

EXPANDING BIT

COUNTERSINK

SCREWDRIVER BIT

MORSE DRILL

RATCHET BRACE

WHEEL BRACE

BRADAWL

POINTED AWL

4 | Hand tool operations

The first operation in the making of a piece of joinery is the sawing of members to size. This involves cross-cutting to length, and ripping to the required sections. For this purpose the timber is placed on sawing stools as indicated on page 39 (foot).

Working from the cutting lists, each member is cut off to length and, if necessary, ripped into smaller sections. Care should be taken when marking off the lengths to avoid defects such as large knots and shakes. Skill in the use of hand tools can only be acquired by the right kind of practice, and this applies particularly to sawing.

One must always aim at cutting down the centre of the line with the saw kerf on the waste side. Gauge lines will give a greater degree of accuracy than pencil lines.

Enlarged views of sawing operations are illustrated on page 39 (top).

Useful hints on sawing

1   Use the correct saw for the job.
2   Aim at splitting the gauge or pencil line.
3   Work methodically when cutting off, stacking all timber straight.
4   Regular maintenance of the saw is essential.

PLANING

The object of planing timber is to obtain a plane surface and true size. The processes involved in this are:
1   Removal of rough surface, using a jack plane.

2 Planing straight and true, using a trying plane (the largest plane used).
3 Planing smooth, using a smoothing plane.

NOTE The smoothing plane should only be used for finishing processes.

It is necessary in the production of all craft work that there should be a true surface, a point, or a line from which to take dimensions. In woodworking, the surface is indicated by a face mark on one side and one edge of each member. The face side mark has the form of a loop, and the face edge mark is a v-shape. The two marks should always meet, as is shown on page 40. There is a mistaken belief among the inexperienced that the best of the widest sides of a piece of timber is always the face side. This is not so in many cases; the face side of a sash bar, for example, is the narrow side. It is true to say, however, that in most cases the widest side should be selected for this purpose.

Sequence of operations involved in planing

1 Using a jack plane and a trying plane, plane straight and out of twist.

NOTE Winding sticks should be used to test for twist.

2 Plane the edge true and square to the face side, and test with the square as shown on page 40 (second operation).
3 Plane to size. Here gauges are set for both width and thickness, and the waste is planed off to the gauge lines.

NOTE It is usual to plane all the members belonging to one job on the face side and face edge first. The thickness and width gauges can then be set to the smallest section.

Allowances for planing

1·5 mm is allowed on all surfaces for planing. For example, a

50 × 100 mm door stile will finish as 47 × 97 mm. The illustrations
on page 40 (top) show:
(a)   (Nominal) cutting size
(b)   Size planed on one side and one edge
(c)   The finished size.

Useful hints on planing

Follow the correct sequence in planing operations. Stack all
timber straight to avoid twisting. Handle the timber carefully to
avoid finger marks.

JOINTS

The *mortise and tenon* is, perhaps, the most important framing
joint used in carpentry and joinery. The type used varies according
to the class and size of the work, but the operations involved in
making them are the same in every case.

The thickness of a tenon should be not more than a third the
thickness of the framing, and the tenon should be placed if possible
in the centre (see page 41—top). This is only possible, however,
when one is dealing with square framing. Often the position has to
be adjusted to suit the shape of the section, as is illustrated on page
41 (middle).

The operations involved are first, the marking out, second, the
mortising, and third, the tenoning.

Marking out

To illustrate the importance of thinking in terms of a complete
piece of framing, consider a simple cupboard door with two stiles,
a top rail, bottom rail and muntin, which has to be mortised and
tenoned together.

Begin marking out on the face edge, overall size first. Take great
care in setting up the mortise gauge. Stiles must always be set out
in pairs.

The marking out of the five members and the method of setting
up the mortise gauge is illustrated on page 42.

Mortising by hand

Mortises in softwood can be formed with a mallet and chisel alone, but hardwoods often present difficulties and make it necessary to remove some of the waste by boring a series of holes slightly smaller in diameter than the width of the mortise.

Begin the mortise in the centre, driving the chisel in vertically. Withdraw the chisel and make another cut about 3 mm from the first. Repeat this process until the mortise is formed. The sequence of operations is illustrated on page 43 (top):

1 Mortise from back edge
2 Mortise from face edge
3 Cut wedge room.

Tenoning

The forming of tenons involves two sawing operations:
1 The ripping of tenons down to the shoulder line
2 The cutting of the shoulder.
These operations are illustrated on page 43 (foot).

Hints on mortising and tenoning

Take great care in setting the mortise gauge. Use the correct saw for the job in hand; cut to the line, and avoid easing tenons. Cut shoulders exactly square. Pointing of the tenons to help in assembly is unnecessary.

Dovetail joints are used in both carpentry and joinery work. In carpentry the sections are usually square or rectangular, while in joinery work they are generally wide and thin. Dovetailing by hand is a job that needs great care; each operation must be accurately carried out in the right sequence.

In square or rectangular sections the dovetail may be considered as a tenon, since it is at the centre one third the thickness of the section marked A (page 44—top). A common pitch for softwood is one in six, and for hardwood one in seven, but one in six is often suitable for hardwood as well. Sections which are wide and thin require small and numerous dovetails. Usually the size is governed by the sort of chisels available.

Snugly fitting joints can be obtained by following the correct sequence of operations, and the stages involved in the making of each joint are given on pages 45, 46 and 47. The top of page 45 shows the making of open dovetails, with the sockets marked from the pins. Page 45 (foot) shows how a mortise gauge is used to mark both pin and socket.

The making of *dovetail halvings* is shown on page 46 (top). In the case of this joint the pins are cut first, and the sockets are then marked from these. Page 46 (foot) shows the making of open dovetails in a wide, thin material.

NOTE   Here the sockets are cut first and the pins marked from them.

The method for dovetailing a drawer is shown on page 47. The materials (drawer front, sides and back) must be worked to the correct size. Next, the drawer fronts are fitted tightly into the openings, and the backs are cut not more than 1 mm shorter than the fronts, depending on the class of work.

NOTE   The drawer sides are cut in pairs, and the pins marked from the sockets.

When mouldings intersect they may be either *scribed* or *mitred*; if they meet in internal angles the deciding factor is the shape of the moulding. The three mouldings ovolo, ogee, and chamfer (page 48—middle), are suitable for scribing, but bead, round and chamfer mouldings (see page 48—foot) need to be mitred.

Where chamfers are concerned, the rule to remember is that chamfers up to 30° can be successfully scribed, while over 30° they are best mitred.

NOTE   In machine woodworking it is usual to modify the shape of a moulding in order to scribe it successfully.

Methods of scribing by hand and machine are shown on page 45 (top). Page 45 (foot) shows the way to mitre.

BORING FOR BOLTS AND DOWELS

A high degree of accuracy is required in boring, since holes for dowels and bolts used in the jointing together of handrails or boards must be in alignment and in corresponding positions in order for one to get an accurate intersection of the two members.

The methods in common practice are shown on page 50: the first drawing shows a method of boring for dowels in edge joints, and the second shows the operations involved in the bolting of handrails.

NOTE Section templets are used for marking accurately the position of dowels and bolts.

REBATING AND GROOVING

Five hand tools are used in the making of rebates and grooves; these are the plough, the rebate plane, the side fillister, the sash fillister and the badger plane—a plane not often used today.

The sequence of operations involved in rebating and grooving is shown on page 51:
1   The method for forming large rebates
2   The use of a side fillister
3   The use of a sash fillister
4   The method for ploughing
5   Sections formed by ploughing and rebating as found in solid and box framing.

MOULDING WITH HAND TOOLS

Small mouldings are formed with special planes, one for each size and shape of moulding.

To form mouldings of varying shapes and sizes, hollows and rounds are used. The planes are obtainable in half sets of nine hollows and nine rounds. Each plane carries a number from two to eighteen. The methods of moulding are illustrated on page 52.

Notice how the member to be moulded is fastened to the bench with a bench knife.

Practice lessons

1 Working from the scale details and instructions given on page 42:

    (a)   Prepare a workshop rod and timber quantities list for the small panelled door 450 mm high by 350 mm wide.

    (b)   Carry out all the hand operations involved in making the door up to the wedging up stage.

    (c)   Wedge up and finish the door on both faces.

2 Working from the instructions given on page 43:

    (a)   Cut out and prepare the timber to make the drawer illustrated at the foot of page 47.

    (b)   Carry out all the operations involved in making the drawer up to, and including, the glueing up stage.

    (c)   Clean up and fit the drawer into a prepared opening.

3 Working from the scale details given on page 48:

    (a)   Set out a workshop rod for the moulded and rebated casement 450 mm high by 350 mm wide.

    (b)   Carry out all the hand operations involved in making the casement up to the wedging up stage.

    (c)   Wedge up, clean off, and fit and hang the casement into a prepared frame.

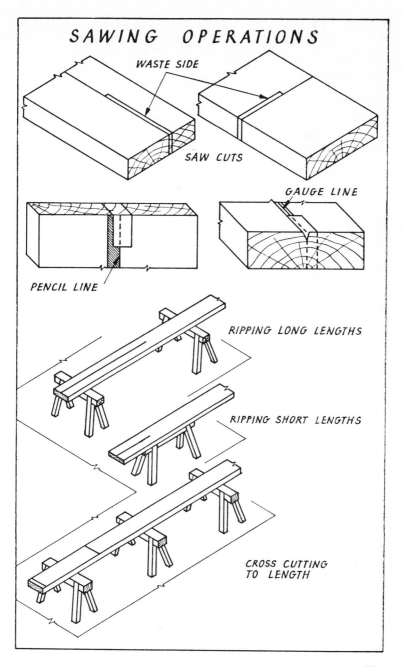

SAWING OPERATIONS

WASTE SIDE

SAW CUTS

GAUGE LINE

PENCIL LINE

RIPPING LONG LENGTHS

RIPPING SHORT LENGTHS

CROSS CUTTING
TO LENGTH

PLANING OPERATIONS

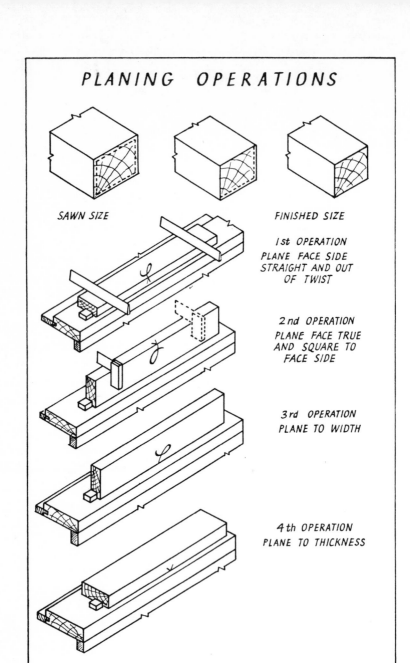

SAWN SIZE

FINISHED SIZE

1st OPERATION
PLANE FACE SIDE
STRAIGHT AND OUT
OF TWIST

2nd OPERATION
PLANE FACE TRUE
AND SQUARE TO
FACE SIDE

3rd OPERATION
PLANE TO WIDTH

4th OPERATION
PLANE TO THICKNESS

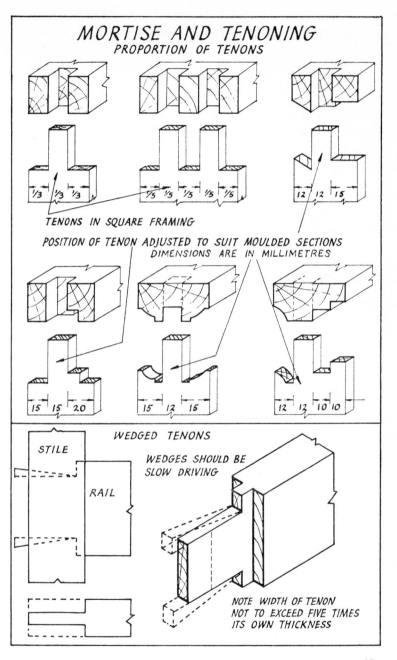

MORTISE AND TENONING
PROPORTION OF TENONS

1/3 1/3 1/3

1/5 1/5 1/5 1/5 1/5

12 12 15

TENONS IN SQUARE FRAMING

POSITION OF TENON ADJUSTED TO SUIT MOULDED SECTIONS
DIMENSIONS ARE IN MILLIMETRES

15 15 20

15 12 15

12 12 10 10

WEDGED TENONS

STILE

RAIL

WEDGES SHOULD BE
SLOW DRIVING

NOTE WIDTH OF TENON
NOT TO EXCEED FIVE TIMES
ITS OWN THICKNESS

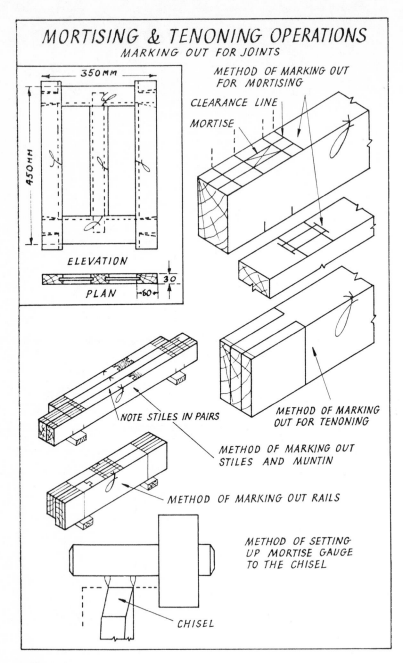

MORTISING & TENONING OPERATIONS
MARKING OUT FOR JOINTS

350MM

450MM

METHOD OF MARKING OUT
FOR MORTISING

CLEARANCE LINE

MORTISE

ELEVATION

PLAN 30 60

METHOD OF MARKING
OUT FOR TENONING

NOTE STILES IN PAIRS

METHOD OF MARKING OUT
STILES AND MUNTIN

METHOD OF MARKING OUT RAILS

METHOD OF SETTING
UP MORTISE GAUGE
TO THE CHISEL

CHISEL

MORTISING & TENONING OPERATIONS
MORTISING

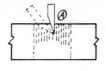

METHOD OF FORMING MORTISE
START IN THE CENTRE Ⓐ
AND WORK OUT

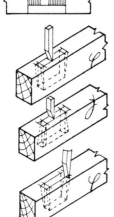

1st OPERATION
START MORTISING FROM
THE BACK EDGE

2nd OPERATION
COMPLETE THE MORTISE
FROM THE FACE EDGE

3rd OPERATION
FORM THE WEDGE ROOM

TENONING

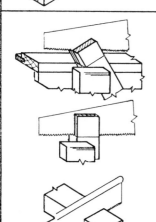

1st OPERATION
RIP THE FIRST HALF OF THE
TENON WITH THE MEMBER
IN A RAKING POSITION

2nd OPERATION
COMPLETE THE CUT WITH THE
MEMBER IN AN UPRIGHT POSITION

3rd OPERATION
SHOULDER CUTTING

NOTE ALL MOULDING, GROOVING
AND REBATING SHOULD BE DONE
BEFORE THE SHOULDERS ARE CUT

DOVETAILS
PROPORTIONS AND PITCH OF PINS

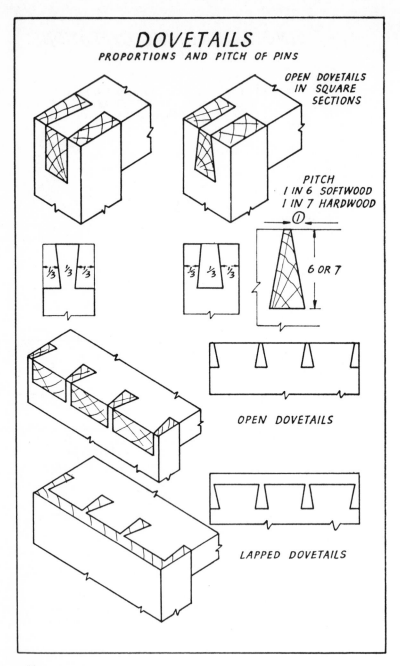

OPEN DOVETAILS
IN SQUARE
SECTIONS

PITCH
1 IN 6 SOFTWOOD
1 IN 7 HARDWOOD

6 OR 7

OPEN DOVETAILS

LAPPED DOVETAILS

DOVETAILING

OPERATIONS INVOLVED IN MAKING EACH JOINT

JOINT TO BE MADE

1st OPERATION
MARKING OUT

2nd OPERATION
CUTTING PINS

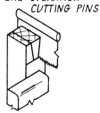

3rd OPERATION
MARKING AND CUTTING
SOCKETS FROM PINS

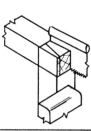

JOINT TO BE MADE

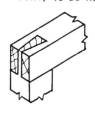

SOCKET
PIN

1st OPERATION
MARKING OUT

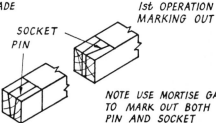

NOTE USE MORTISE GAUGE
TO MARK OUT BOTH
PIN AND SOCKET

2nd & 3rd OPERATION
CUTTING PINS AND SOCKETS

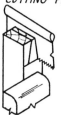

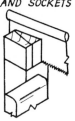

4th OPERATION
CUT SHOULDERS
AND ASSEMBLE

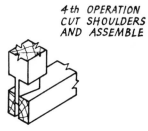

DOVETAILING
OPERATIONS INVOLVED IN MAKING EACH JOINT

 JOINT

 1st & 2nd OPERATION MARK OUT AND CUT PIN

3rd OPERATION MARK SOCKETS FROM PINS

4th OPERATION SAW SOCKETS

5th OPERATION ASSEMBLE

JOINT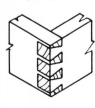

① OPERATION MARK OUT AND CUT SOCKETS

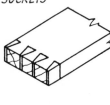

② MARK PINS FROM SOCKETS

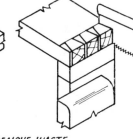

③ CUT PINS

④ & ⑤ REMOVE WASTE

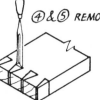

⑥ ASSEMBLE JOINT

46

DOVETAILING
OPERATIONS INVOLVED IN DOVETAILING A DRAWER

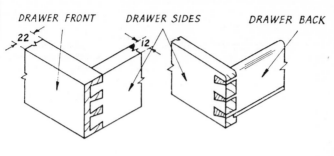

DRAWER FRONT   DRAWER SIDES   DRAWER BACK

22

12

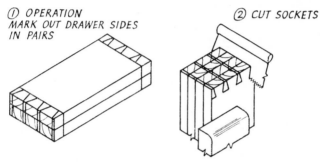

① OPERATION
MARK OUT DRAWER SIDES
IN PAIRS

② CUT SOCKETS

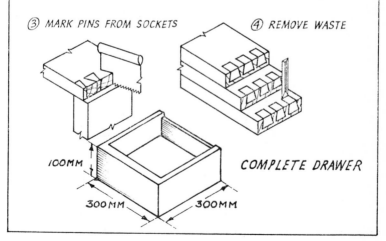

③ MARK PINS FROM SOCKETS

④ REMOVE WASTE

100MM

COMPLETE DRAWER

300MM   300MM

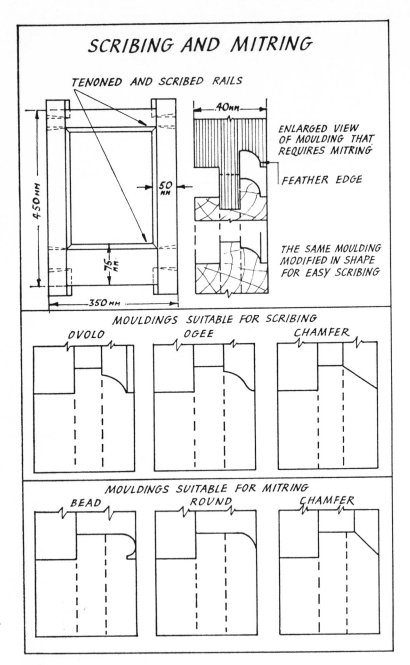

SCRIBING AND MITRING

TENONED AND SCRIBED RAILS

450 MM

75 MM

350 MM

50 MM

40 MM

ENLARGED VIEW OF MOULDING THAT REQUIRES MITRING

FEATHER EDGE

THE SAME MOULDING MODIFIED IN SHAPE FOR EASY SCRIBING

MOULDINGS SUITABLE FOR SCRIBING

OVOLO   OGEE   CHAMFER

MOULDINGS SUITABLE FOR MITRING

BEAD   ROUND   CHAMFER

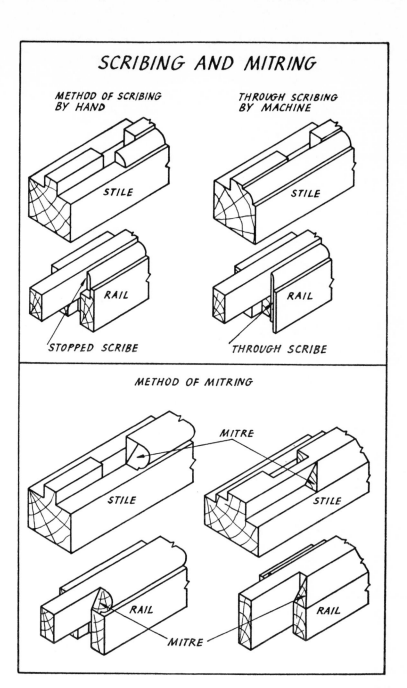

SCRIBING AND MITRING

METHOD OF SCRIBING BY HAND

STILE

RAIL

STOPPED SCRIBE

THROUGH SCRIBING BY MACHINE

STILE

RAIL

THROUGH SCRIBE

METHOD OF MITRING

MITRE

STILE

STILE

RAIL

RAIL

MITRE

BORING FOR BOLTS AND DOWELS

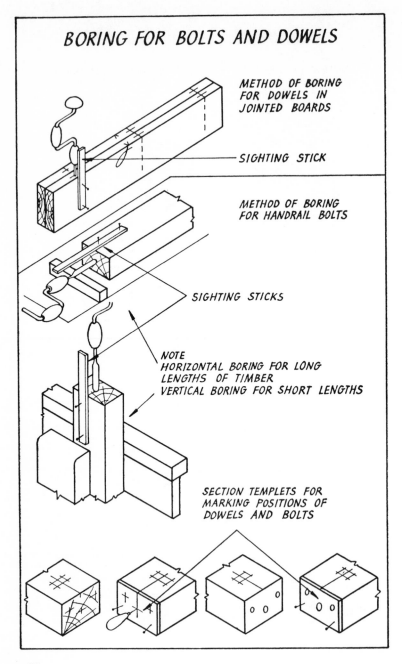

METHOD OF BORING
FOR DOWELS IN
JOINTED BOARDS

SIGHTING STICK

METHOD OF BORING
FOR HANDRAIL BOLTS

SIGHTING STICKS

NOTE
HORIZONTAL BORING FOR LONG
LENGTHS OF TIMBER
VERTICAL BORING FOR SHORT LENGTHS

SECTION TEMPLETS FOR
MARKING POSITIONS OF
DOWELS AND BOLTS

REBATING AND GROOVING

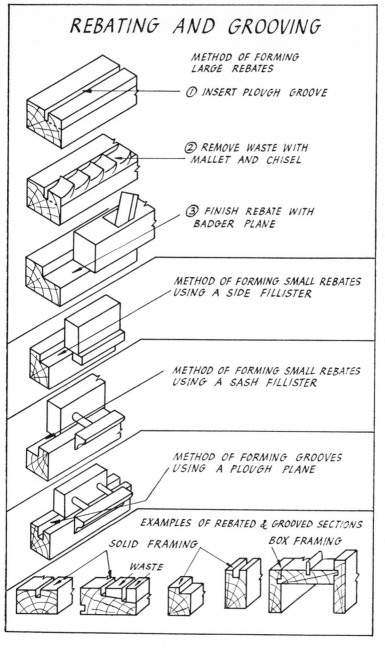

METHOD OF FORMING
LARGE REBATES

① INSERT PLOUGH GROOVE

② REMOVE WASTE WITH
MALLET AND CHISEL

③ FINISH REBATE WITH
BADGER PLANE

METHOD OF FORMING SMALL REBATES
USING A SIDE FILLISTER

METHOD OF FORMING SMALL REBATES
USING A SASH FILLISTER

METHOD OF FORMING GROOVES
USING A PLOUGH PLANE

EXAMPLES OF REBATED & GROOVED SECTIONS

SOLID FRAMING

BOX FRAMING

WASTE

MOULDING

METHOD OF FORMING MOULDINGS USING HAND PLANES

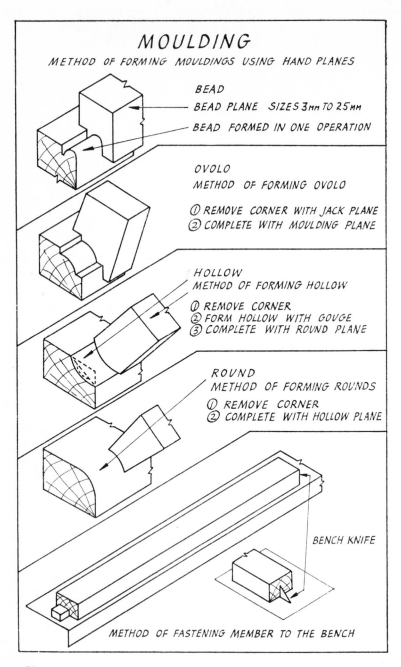

BEAD

BEAD PLANE   SIZES 3mm TO 25mm

BEAD FORMED IN ONE OPERATION

OVOLO

METHOD OF FORMING OVOLO

① REMOVE CORNER WITH JACK PLANE
② COMPLETE WITH MOULDING PLANE

HOLLOW

METHOD OF FORMING HOLLOW

① REMOVE CORNER
② FORM HOLLOW WITH GOUGE
③ COMPLETE WITH ROUND PLANE

ROUND

METHOD OF FORMING ROUNDS

① REMOVE CORNER
② COMPLETE WITH HOLLOW PLANE

BENCH KNIFE

METHOD OF FASTENING MEMBER TO THE BENCH

5 | Woodworking machines and machine operations

The working of timber by machine has become a highly developed and specialised process. Machines and machine tools have been designed to carry out, at high speed, all the operations that were previously executed by hand, and they can do practically everything—sawing, planing, rebating, grooving, moulding, mortising, tenoning, scribing, dovetailing, sanding and finishing. The machine is no longer regarded simply as a device for relieving the hand craftsman of heavy work.

Machine operations

Three main processes are involved in the manufacture of joinery work:
1 Cutting out and planing to size
2 Jointing and shaping
3 Finishing.
A chart showing the machines and operations involved is given at the top of page 58.

Types of cutting heads

The cutting units on the majority of woodworking machines used in the manufacture of joinery may be classified as saws or cutter blocks. Saws may be further classified as circular saws or band saws; and cutter blocks as square, circular, or slotted collars, or solid profile.

Sawing machines used in the manufacture of joinery

Circular saws, hand operated in the smaller shops and mechanically fed in the larger shops, are used mainly for breaking down large sections into the smaller sections required for the job.

The *narrow band saw* can be from 3 to 36 mm wide, and is extensively used for curved sawing. With care it will also do deep cutting quite satisfactorily.

The shapes of the teeth on circular and band saws are very similar to those on hand saws, except that they have a positive hook instead of a negative one.

Machines and saw teeth are shown on pages 58 (foot) and 59 (top).

NOTE   The angles of the hook and clean rounded gullets vary.

The rim speed of the saw is very important. It varies from 2,800 metres per minute in the case of rip saws, to 4,300 metres for clean-cutting dimension saws. The speed in revolutions per minute will alter with the size of the saw. Small saws will have a high r.p.m., large saws a low r.p.m.

Four common saw-milling processes are illustrated on page 59 (foot):
1   Ripping (sawing the narrow way of the plank or deal)
2   Deeping (sawing the wider way of the plank or deal)
3   Splay cutting (sawing diagonally)
4   Curved cutting (circular sawing).

Planing machines used in the manufacture of joinery

The diagrams on page 60 (foot) illustrate the planing action of *rotary cutters.* The revolving cutters form ridges, called cuts, and the width of each cut governs the standard of finish. Four cuts to 25 mm would be considered very poor, and twenty cuts to 25 mm would be thought good.

Surface planers are used for planing straight and out of twist. All these machines, when operated by hand, must be fitted with a circular cutter block for safety. A machine, with its block, is shown on page 60 (top).

Thickness planers are used for bringing the timber to size. The majority of these machines have mechanical feeds, and may be fitted with square or circular blocks. A detail of the cutter block and mechanical feed is shown on page 61 (top).

Four siders are used for planing all the sides in one operation.

The speed on the cutting circle is between 1,700 and 1,900 metres per minute. As in the case of saws, the speed in revolutions per minute is dependent on the size of the blocks.

It is essential, if high standards in surface finish are required, that each cutter should be accurately set on the cutting circle. Many thicknessing machines have four cutters on the block, and if only one cutter is actually finishing the surface the machine will naturally only be a quarter as efficient as it should be.

The main function of surface planers and thicknessers is to plane timber flat and true to size. There are, however, other operations that can be successfully carried out on planing machines. Rebating, chamfering and tapering by this method are shown on page 61 (foot).

Jointmaking and shaping machines

Three machines are involved in this work, and they are usually group operated. They are the mortise machine, the tenoning machine, and the spindle moulder.

NOTE In the larger shops, spindle moulders and four sider cutters would be used.

A combined chisel and chain *mortise machine* is illustrated on page 62, together with details of the hollow chisels and chain cutting gear.

A *tenoning and scribing machine* has two horizontal cutting heads, which form the tenon, and two vertical heads, which form the scribings on each side of the tenoned members. Details of the tenoning and scribing heads are given on page 63.

The *spindle moulder* has a vertical spindle on which various interchangeable cutting heads may be used. The machine and details of the cutter blocks are shown on page 64.

The spindle operation is illustrated on page 65, together with the types of cutting heads used with it:

1 The working, with a square block, of rebated and moulded framing
2 The method of rebating with a slotted collar cutting head
3 How to mould using a french head
4 A whitehill, thin cutter block in the process of chamfering
5 How to groove with a drunken saw.

Safety precautions

Home Office Regulations state that all woodworking machinery must be effectively guarded. A circular saw must have an adjustable top guard covering the gullet depth, and a riving knife not more than 12 mm from the back of the saw. All hand operated surface planers must be fitted with adjustable bridge guards. Mortise chains must be fitted with guards which completely cover the chain. Spindle moulders must be fitted with adjustable cage or Shaw guards, or alternatively with effective guards of approved design. All mechanically fed machines must have cutting heads, feed units, pulleys and belts completely covered.

Operatives should make full use of the equipment designed for their safety. Push sticks, spring fences and jigs all contribute towards the safe working of small units.

Practice lessons

1   Working from the information given on pages 58–59:

   (a)   Make neat diagrams of the teeth of a circular saw suitable for ripping softwood. Show clearly the angle of hook and the clearance angle.
   (b)   Show the position of the top guard and riving knife on a circular saw bench, and explain why they are necessary.
   (c)   Explain the sawing operations, ripping, deeping and splay cutting.

2   Working from the information given on page 60:

   (a)   Draw full size the cross-section of a surface planer block, showing the position of the cutters in the block, and the cutting and clearance angles.
   (b)   Make neat diagrams to explain the theory of planing by rotary cutters.
   (c)   Make a neat diagram of a bridge guard and explain its function.

3   Working from the information given on pages 61–62 and 65, make neat sketches to explain the following machine operations:

   (a)   Mortising with a hollow chisel.
   (b)   Rebating on a surface planer.
   (c)   Grooving with a drunken saw.

WOODWORKING MACHINES
MACHINE OPERATIONS

CUTTING OUT AND PLANING TO SIZE	JOINTING AND SHAPING	FINISHING
MACHINES INVOLVED		
CIRCULAR SAWS BAND SAWS SURFACE PLANERS THICKNESS PLANERS	MORTISE MACHINES TENONING MACHINES SPINDLE MOULDERS FOUR CUTTERS ROUTERS	CRAMPS PRESSES GLUE SPREADERS SANDERS

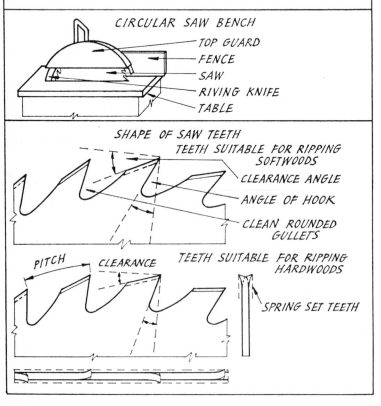

CIRCULAR SAW BENCH

— TOP GUARD
— FENCE
— SAW
— RIVING KNIFE
— TABLE

SHAPE OF SAW TEETH

TEETH SUITABLE FOR RIPPING SOFTWOODS

CLEARANCE ANGLE

ANGLE OF HOOK

CLEAN ROUNDED GULLETS

PITCH   CLEARANCE

TEETH SUITABLE FOR RIPPING HARDWOODS

SPRING SET TEETH

WOODWORKING MACHINES

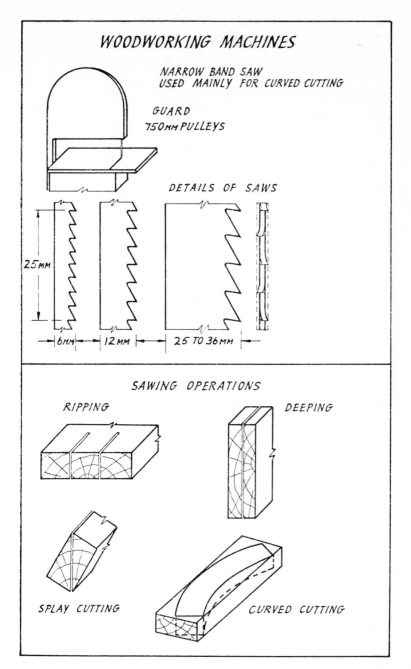

NARROW BAND SAW
USED MAINLY FOR CURVED CUTTING

GUARD
750mm PULLEYS

DETAILS OF SAWS

25mm

6mm | 12mm | 25 TO 36mm

SAWING OPERATIONS

RIPPING

DEEPING

SPLAY CUTTING

CURVED CUTTING

WOODWORKING MACHINES
SURFACE PLANING MACHINES

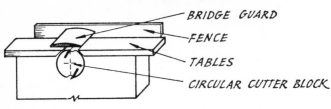

BRIDGE GUARD

FENCE

TABLES

CIRCULAR CUTTER BLOCK

DETAILS OF CIRCULAR CUTTER BLOCK

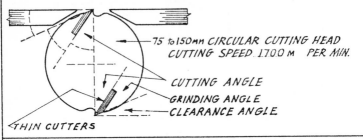

75 to 150mm CIRCULAR CUTTING HEAD
CUTTING SPEED 1700 m PER MIN.

CUTTING ANGLE

GRINDING ANGLE
CLEARANCE ANGLE

THIN CUTTERS

THE THEORY OF PLANING BY ROTARY CUTTERS
ENLARGED VIEW OF PLANED FINISH

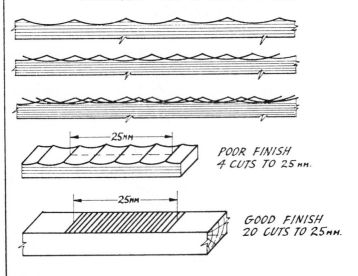

25mm

POOR FINISH
4 CUTS TO 25 mm.

25mm

GOOD FINISH
20 CUTS TO 25 mm.

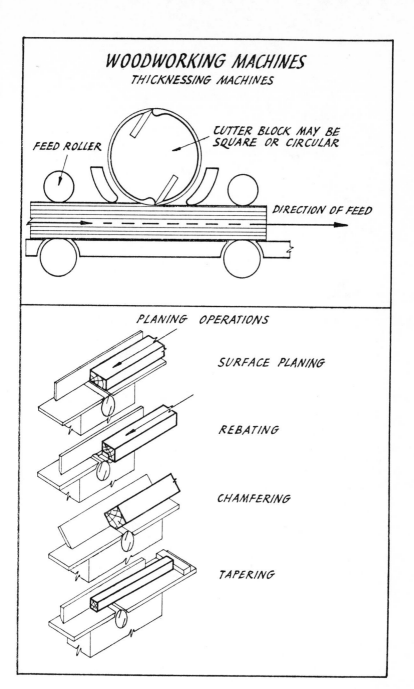

WOODWORKING MACHINES
THICKNESSING MACHINES

CUTTER BLOCK MAY BE
SQUARE OR CIRCULAR

FEED ROLLER

DIRECTION OF FEED

PLANING OPERATIONS

SURFACE PLANING

REBATING

CHAMFERING

TAPERING

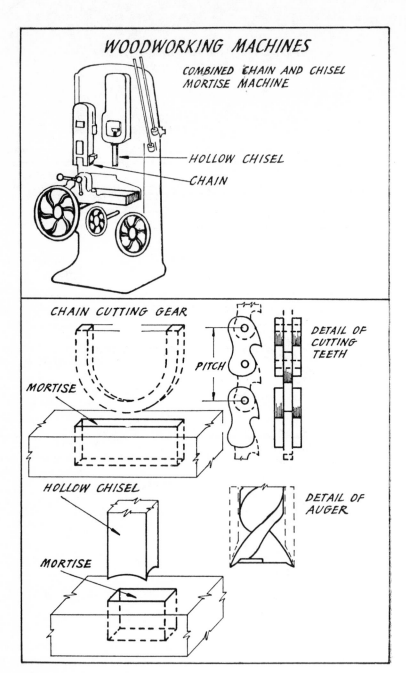

WOODWORKING MACHINES

COMBINED CHAIN AND CHISEL
MORTISE MACHINE

HOLLOW CHISEL

CHAIN

CHAIN CUTTING GEAR

PITCH

MORTISE

DETAIL OF
CUTTING
TEETH

HOLLOW CHISEL

MORTISE

DETAIL OF
AUGER

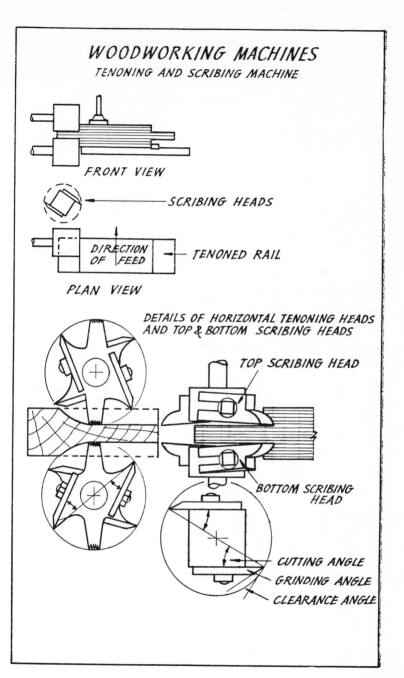

WOODWORKING MACHINES
TENONING AND SCRIBING MACHINE

FRONT VIEW

SCRIBING HEADS

DIRECTION OF FEED — TENONED RAIL

PLAN VIEW

DETAILS OF HORIZONTAL TENONING HEADS AND TOP & BOTTOM SCRIBING HEADS

TOP SCRIBING HEAD

BOTTOM SCRIBING HEAD

CUTTING ANGLE
GRINDING ANGLE
CLEARANCE ANGLE

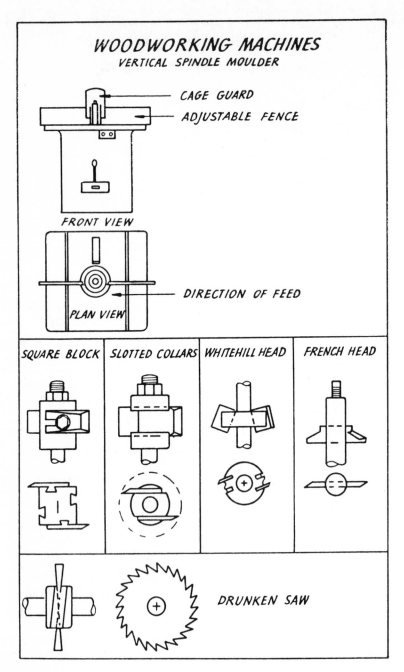

WOODWORKING MACHINES
VERTICAL SPINDLE MOULDER

CAGE GUARD

ADJUSTABLE FENCE

FRONT VIEW

DIRECTION OF FEED

PLAN VIEW

SQUARE BLOCK

SLOTTED COLLARS

WHITEHILL HEAD

FRENCH HEAD

DRUNKEN SAW

WOODWORKING MACHINES
VERTICAL SPINDLE MOULDER OPERATIONS

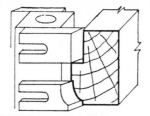

SQUARE CUTTER BLOCK FOR
MOULDING AND REBATING

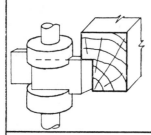

SLOTTED COLLARS FOR
REBATING

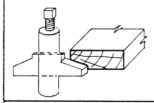

FRENCH HEAD FOR MOULDING

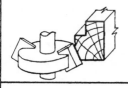

WHITEHILL HEAD FOR CHAMFERING

DRUNKEN SAW FOR GROOVING

6 | Timber floors

Timber is now mainly used for structural members only in domestic buildings, since concrete and other fire resistant materials are preferable for larger building work. It is, however, used extensively for floor coverings, especially when these are intended to be decorative.

Timber floors consist of a series of joists spanning from wall to wall, and supporting a thin floor covering.

Fireplace openings

Fireplace openings present difficulties in construction. Because of the risk of fire, no timber must be built into a flue, or used less than 400 mm from the front or 150 mm from the side of any fireplace opening. On suspended floors, joists of larger section (usually thicker by 12 mm to 25 mm), termed trimmers and trimming joists, are used to support the fireplace end of the trimmed joist.

Floors may be classified as ground floors or upper floors. In the case of ground floors, the joists are supported along their length by sleeper walls. The joists on the upper floors have no intermediate support, and therefore they need to be of greater depth—approximately twice that of ground-floor joists.

GROUND FLOORS

The plans of two typical ground floors are shown on page 73. The joists in the first are at right angles to the chimney breast, and in the second they are parallel to it.

Size and spacing of timbers

Sections in common use are those 63 × 100 mm and 63 × 125 mm. The thickness of the floor covering will govern the spacing of the joists. 18 mm floor boards require support every 300 to 375 mm, whereas 25–30 mm floor boards require support every 375 to 450 mm.

Support of joists

The bearing on the walls at the ends of each joist must be at least 115 mm. Intermediate support, at intervals of 2 to 3 metres, is given by 115 mm sleeper walls, honeycombed to provide through ventilation.

The fixing of ground-floor joists

The fixing of the ground-floor joists is usually the first carpentry job on a new building. The joists, after being cut off to length, are laid on the walls and levelled. Care must be taken to keep the joist in position during the building-in. Laths are nailed at each end of the joists, coupling the joists together (see page 74—top).

Prevention of dampness

All buildings must be provided with a horizontal damp-proof course, placed 150 mm above the ground, and extending through all external and internal walls. Timber should not be placed below this level. This is illustrated at the foot of page 73.

All timber ground floors must be adequately ventilated. Through ventilation is provided by air grids, and by the honeycombing of sleeper walls. Air grids must be placed on opposite walls in order to give a free passage to air under the floor.

UPPER FLOORS

The plans of two typical upper floors are shown on page 74 (foot). The joists should always span the short way of the room.

Floor timbers

1   *Bridging joists* are single joists spanning an opening.
2   *Trimming joists* are main joists spanning an opening into which
the trimmer joist is framed.
3   *Trimmers* are main cross joists supported at their ends by the
trimming joists.
4   *Trimmed joists* are joists supported by the wall at one end, and
framed into the trimmer at the other.

The fixing of upper-floor joists

When a building has reached the first floor level, the joists are
placed in position. The main timbers will require jointing. The
setting out of each main member, trimmer, trimming joist and
trimmed joist, is illustrated on page 74.

Method of framing joists together

The joint used for this purpose in floors is called a tusk tenon
joint, and is designed to give maximum strength.

FLOORS (GENERAL)

Design of structural members

The shape and size of structural members (joists) of a timber floor
may be determined in two ways (a) by a study of the relative effect
of the span, breadth and depth on the strength of a joist or beam,
and (b) by equating the moment of the external forces with the
moment of the internal resistance forces. To do this a knowledge
of the theory of structures and mechanics is necessary. The method
(a) is more easily understood than method (b) when one has a
limited knowledge of science and mathematics but because of its
accuracy the general practice today is to use the method of equating
the external moments of force with the internal moments of
resistance.

The practical application of method (b) is given on page 75.

Proportions of joists

The bending stresses set up in the joists, caused by the load on the floor, are shown on page 75 (top). The maximum stress occurs on the top and bottom edges with no stress occurring at the point midway through the depth. For a plan of stress distribution, see page 75 (middle). Mortises must be placed
1 in the area of minimum stress.
2 If possible, within the compression area of the joist.
    The proportions of the joist are given on page 76 (foot).

NOTE   The thickness of the tenon $= \frac{1}{6}$ depth of joist.
        Depth of tusk $= \frac{1}{6}$ thickness of joist.
        Length of tenon $= 150$ mm past wedge.
    A simple rule-of-thumb method for finding the approximate joist section is as follows:
    Divide the span (*in decimetres*) by 2 and add 2. This will give the depth of the joist *in centimetres*.
EXAMPLE   Span 4·2 metres

$$\text{Depth of joist} = \frac{\text{span}}{2} + 2$$

$$= \frac{42}{2} + 2$$

$$= 230 \text{ mm}$$

The breadth may be taken as one third the depth, giving a joist section of 75×225 mm.

Strutting

Strutting is necessary to give stability to the floor and to prevent any tendency to buckle and thus cause deflection under the maximum floor load.
    Herring-bone strutting is extensively used on domestic building. It consists of a row of struts cut diagonally between the joists as illustrated on page 77 (foot).
    Solid strutting, the traditional method of construction for large buildings, has now been replaced by other forms of floor construction.

Floor coverings

The traditional type of floor covering is boards, which may be nailed through the face or secret nailed. Softwood floor boards are usually tongued and grooved together, then nailed through the face with floor brads. Details of tongued and grooved softwood floor boards are given in page 78 (top).

The width of each board should not exceed 125 mm in order to minimise shrinkage. The tongue and groove is placed out of centre, thus giving a longer wearing surface to the board (page 78—middle).

Hardwood floors are usually in strip form, with a maximum width on face of 75 mm. Details of the boards are given on page 79 (foot). The tongues and grooves are of a special shape to allow for secret nailing.

Heading joints may be butted, splayed or rebated. No two heading joints should meet on the same joist (see page 79—foot).

Method of laying floor boards

The floor laying operation follows the roofing-in of the building. The traditional way of seasoning the floor boards before laying is to place them in a triangular stack as illustrated on page 80 (middle).

After the margin has been formed or the first board prepared, begin laying boards from the hearth as shown (page 80—top). The laying operation includes cutting to length, the cramping together of the boards with special floor cramps, and finally, nailing.

Brads are used for nailing the boards to the joist. The length of the brad should be $2\frac{1}{2}$ times the thickness of the board. Two nails are required in each board on each joist, and all nails should be punched in as the work proceeds.

Cleaning off

Today, the cleaning-off operation is mechanised, and is done with special floor sanders, designed to clean off any type of soft- or hardwood floor. The traditional way of cleaning off a hardwood floor by hand is to plane and scrape it.

Protection of floors after laying

It is essential to protect all floor surfaces from damage while the building is being finished. Planer shavings, sawdust, and felt sheets are often used for this purpose.

Practice lessons

1 Working from the information given:

   (a) Draw the ground floor plan of a room as shown on page 73. Scale 1:20.

   (b) Show position of the floor joists, fender and sleeper walls, and the fireplace construction.

   (c) Make 1:5 scale drawings to show how the floor is ventilated, and the prevention of dampness.

2 *(a)* Draw the square plan of the upper floor room, as shown on page 74. Scale 1:20.

   (b) Show on the plan the position of all the floor timbers and give their sectional size.

   (c) Make a neat diagram to show the nature of the bending stresses set up in a floor joist.

   (d) Give details, and show the proportions of the tusk tenon framing joint used.

   (e) Give details of the floor strutting, and explain its function.

3 *(a)* Draw, full size, the sectional view of two types of floor boards, giving clear details of the edge and heading joints.

   (b) Give details of the method of fixing floor boards, and the type, and size, of nails used.

TIMBER FLOORS
GROUND FLOORS

JOISTS AT RIGHT ANGLES TO FIREPLACE OPENING

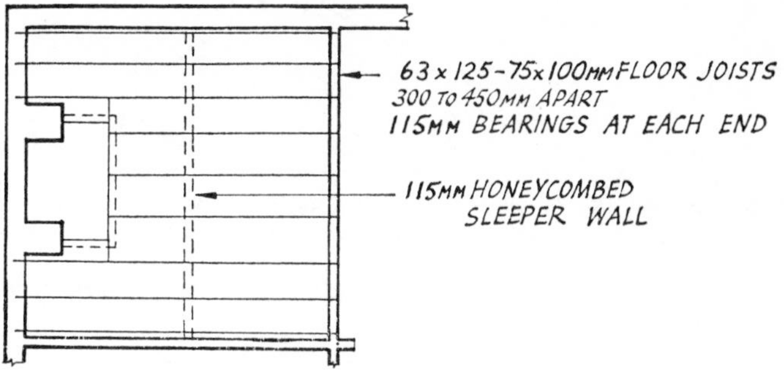

— 63 x 125 – 75 x 100mm FLOOR JOISTS
300 TO 450mm APART
115mm BEARINGS AT EACH END

— 115mm HONEYCOMBED
SLEEPER WALL

JOISTS PARALLEL TO FIREPLACE OPENING

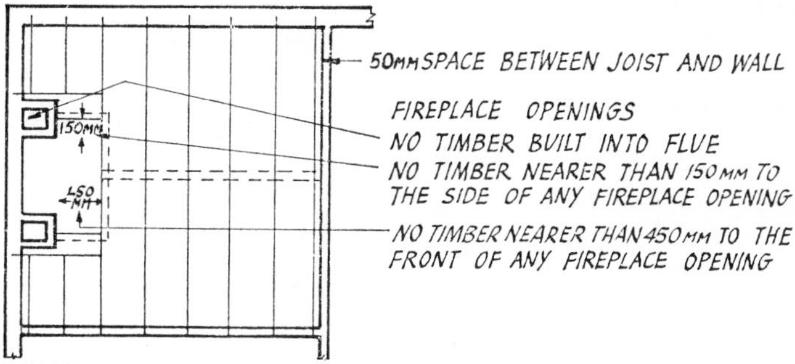

150mm

L50 MM

— 50mm SPACE BETWEEN JOIST AND WALL

FIREPLACE OPENINGS
NO TIMBER BUILT INTO FLUE
NO TIMBER NEARER THAN 150mm TO
THE SIDE OF ANY FIREPLACE OPENING

— NO TIMBER NEARER THAN 450mm TO THE
FRONT OF ANY FIREPLACE OPENING

PREVENTION OF DAMPNESS

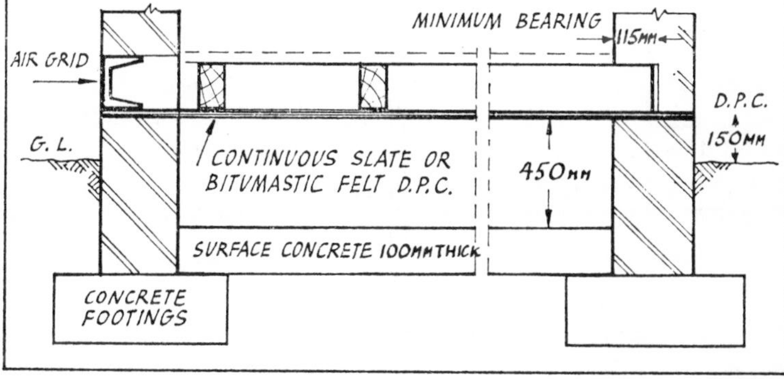

MINIMUM BEARING

115mm

AIR GRID

G. L.

D.P.C.
150mm

CONTINUOUS SLATE OR
BITUMASTIC FELT D.P.C.

450mm

SURFACE CONCRETE 100mm THICK

CONCRETE
FOOTINGS

73

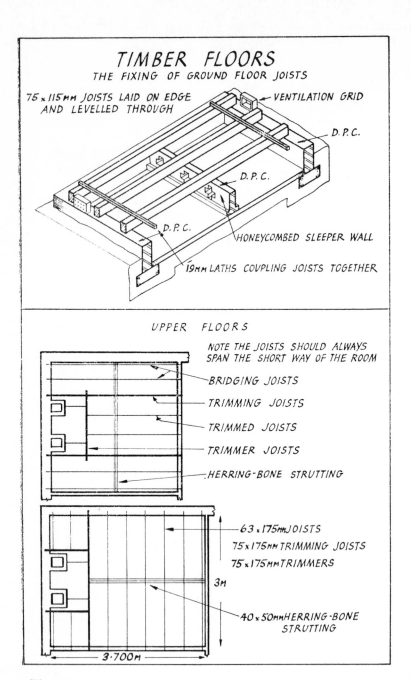

TIMBER FLOORS
THE FIXING OF GROUND FLOOR JOISTS

75 × 115mm JOISTS LAID ON EDGE AND LEVELLED THROUGH

VENTILATION GRID

D.P.C.

D.P.C.

D.P.C.

HONEYCOMBED SLEEPER WALL

19mm LATHS COUPLING JOISTS TOGETHER

UPPER FLOORS

NOTE THE JOISTS SHOULD ALWAYS SPAN THE SHORT WAY OF THE ROOM

BRIDGING JOISTS

TRIMMING JOISTS

TRIMMED JOISTS

TRIMMER JOISTS

HERRING-BONE STRUTTING

63 × 175mm JOISTS

75 × 175mm TRIMMING JOISTS

75 × 175mm TRIMMERS

3M

40 × 50mm HERRING-BONE STRUTTING

3·700M

74

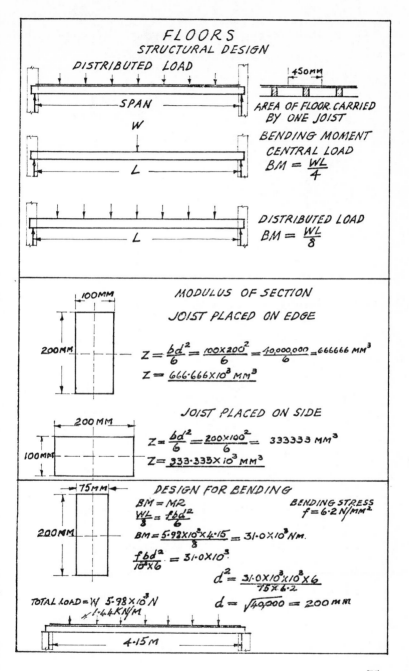

FLOORS
STRUCTURAL DESIGN

DISTRIBUTED LOAD

450mm

AREA OF FLOOR. CARRIED
BY ONE JOIST

BENDING MOMENT
CENTRAL LOAD
$$BM = \frac{WL}{4}$$

SPAN

W

L

L

DISTRIBUTED LOAD
$$BM = \frac{WL}{8}$$

MODULUS OF SECTION

JOIST PLACED ON EDGE

100MM

200MM

$$Z = \frac{bd^2}{6} = \frac{100 \times 200^2}{6} = \frac{40,000,000}{6} = 666666 \ MM^3$$

$$Z = \underline{666.666 \times 10^3 \ MM^3}$$

JOIST PLACED ON SIDE

200 MM

100MM

$$Z = \frac{bd^2}{6} = \frac{200 \times 100^2}{6} = 333333 \ MM^3$$

$$Z = \underline{333.333 \times 10^3 \ MM^3}$$

DESIGN FOR BENDING

75MM

200MM

$$BM = MR$$

$$\frac{WL}{8} = \frac{fbd^2}{6}$$

BENDING STRESS
$$f = 6.2 \ N/MM^2$$

$$BM = \frac{5.98 \times 10^3 \times 4.15}{8} = 31.0 \times 10^3 \ Nm.$$

$$\frac{fbd^2}{10^3 \times 6} = 31.0 \times 10^3.$$

$$d^2 = \frac{31.0 \times 10^3 \times 10^3 \times 6}{75 \times 6.2}$$

$$d = \sqrt{40,000} = 200 \ MM$$

TOTAL LOAD = W $5.98 \times 10^3 N$
× 1.44 KN/M

4.15 M

75

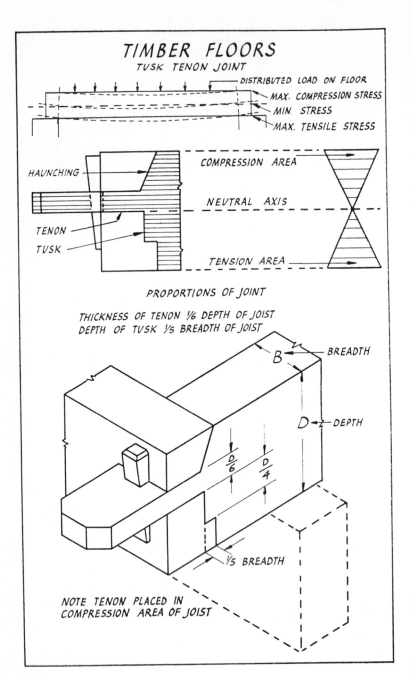

TIMBER FLOORS
TUSK TENON JOINT

DISTRIBUTED LOAD ON FLOOR
MAX. COMPRESSION STRESS
MIN. STRESS
MAX. TENSILE STRESS

HAUNCHING

COMPRESSION AREA

NEUTRAL AXIS

TENON

TUSK

TENSION AREA

PROPORTIONS OF JOINT

THICKNESS OF TENON ⅙ DEPTH OF JOIST
DEPTH OF TUSK ⅕ BREADTH OF JOIST

BREADTH
B
D — DEPTH

$\frac{D}{6}$
$\frac{D}{4}$

⅕ BREADTH

NOTE TENON PLACED IN
COMPRESSION AREA OF JOIST

76

TIMBER FLOORS
THE FIXING OF UPPER FLOOR JOISTS

METHOD OF MARKING OUT MEMBERS THAT REQUIRE JOINTING
SEE UPPER FLOOR PLANS

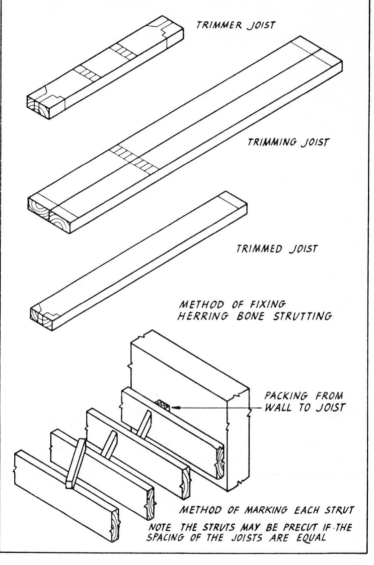

TRIMMER JOIST

TRIMMING JOIST

TRIMMED JOIST

METHOD OF FIXING
HERRING BONE STRUTTING

PACKING FROM
WALL TO JOIST

METHOD OF MARKING EACH STRUT

NOTE THE STRUTS MAY BE PRECUT IF THE
SPACING OF THE JOISTS ARE EQUAL

TIMBER FLOORS
SOFTWOOD FLOOR COVERINGS

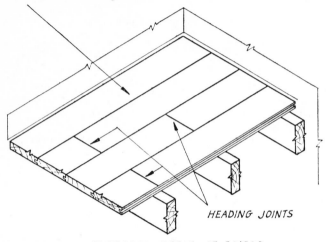

25 × 125mm T & G FLOOR BOARDS
LAID ON 63 × 175mm JOISTS

HEADING JOINTS

ENLARGED DETAIL OF BOARDS

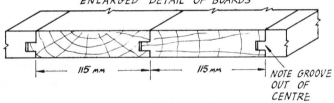

115 mm   115 mm   NOTE GROOVE
OUT OF
CENTRE

TYPES OF HEADING JOINTS

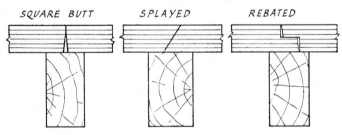

SQUARE BUTT   SPLAYED   REBATED

TIMBER FLOORS
HARDWOOD FLOOR COVERINGS

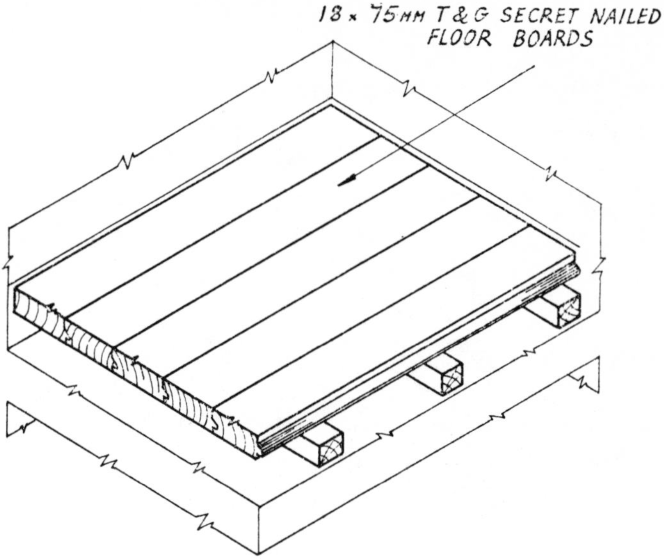

18 × 75MM T&G SECRET NAILED
FLOOR BOARDS

ENLARGED DETAIL OF BOARDS

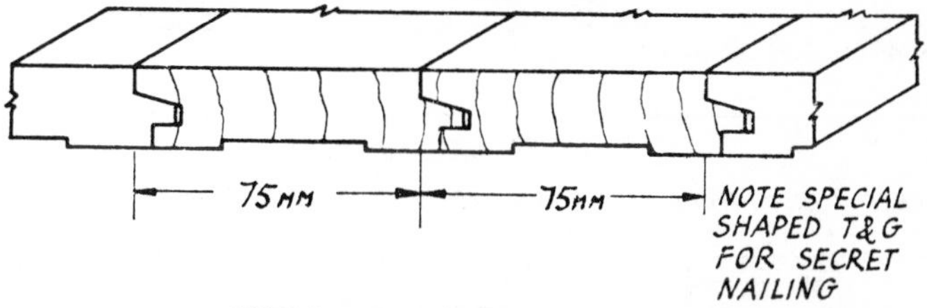

75MM — 75MM — NOTE SPECIAL
SHAPED T&G
FOR SECRET
NAILING

TYPES OF HEADING JOINTS

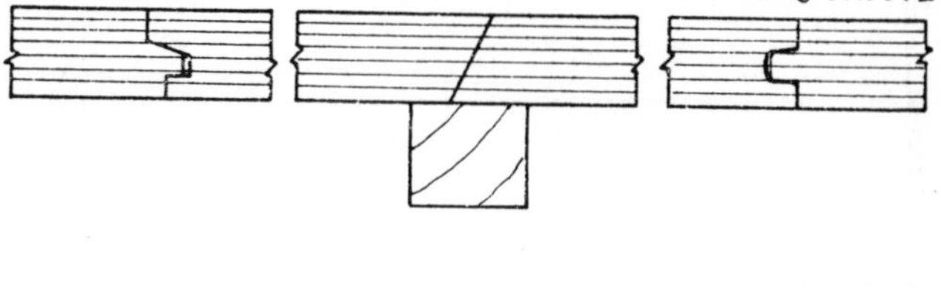

T&G TO MATCH
EDGE JOINT   SPLAYED   TONGUE & GROOVE

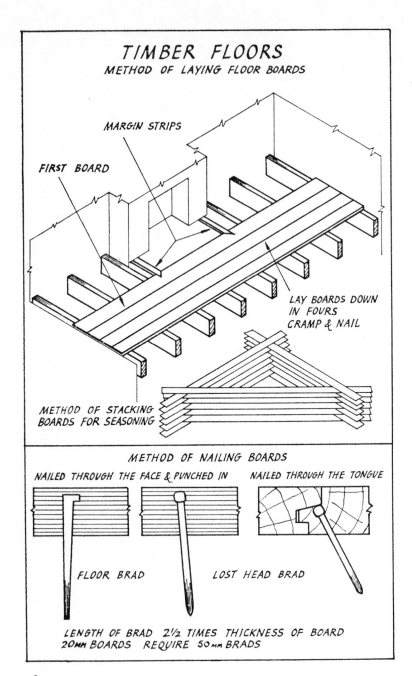

TIMBER FLOORS
METHOD OF LAYING FLOOR BOARDS

MARGIN STRIPS

FIRST BOARD

LAY BOARDS DOWN
IN FOURS
CRAMP & NAIL

METHOD OF STACKING
BOARDS FOR SEASONING

METHOD OF NAILING BOARDS

NAILED THROUGH THE FACE & PUNCHED IN   NAILED THROUGH THE TONGUE

FLOOR BRAD   LOST HEAD BRAD

LENGTH OF BRAD 2½ TIMES THICKNESS OF BOARD
20mm BOARDS REQUIRE 50mm BRADS

7 Roofs

Timber roofs may be classified according to their shape. The four most common types are the flat roof, the lean-to or pent roof, the span, couple or gable roof, and the hipped ridge roof. All these are illustrated on page 89.

Roof pitch

The pitch will be governed by the unit size and type of roof covering used. Non-porous materials, such as lead, copper, and asphalt, are suitable for flat roofs. A pitch of 10° or more is required for large asbestos or metal sheets, 30° for large non-porous slates, and 40° to 60° for small slates and porous tiles. They are shown on page 90.

Structural design

It is essential that a roof structure should remain rigid. To ensure this a triangular shaped construction must be used, since this is the only shape that cannot be distorted. The efficiency of a triangular shaped construction may be proved by experiment. For example, the square frame shown on page 91 (top) can easily be distorted, but by the introduction of a diagonal it becomes a rigid frame.

All six constructions on page 91 (middle), which are called perfect frames, are triangular shaped and therefore cannot be distorted, whereas the two diagrams on page 91 (foot) are not perfect frames, and distortion can take place.

It is also necessary to discover the nature and magnitude of the stresses in the structural members. These can be resolved graphically, and to do this a knowledge of graphic statics and mechanics is necessary. The external loads to be carried by the roof structure are:

1 Dead loads, consisting of weight of roof covering, weight of purlins, and weight of trusses.

2 Wind loads, which only act on one side of the roof at a time.

The nature of the stresses in structural members of a roof can be best explained in diagram form (see page 92):

1 Shows that the pitched rafters tend to spread the walls. The nature of the stress (compression) in the rafter is indicated by arrows pointing towards the joint.

2 Page 92 (2) shows the introduction of the tie to prevent spreading. The stress (tensile) is indicated by arrows pointing towards the centre.

As the span of the roof increases, the tie tends to deflect and a vertical tie is introduced to prevent this. The stress in this member is also tensile. As the span increases still further, the rafters will naturally be longer, and will tend to bend (see page 92 (3)). To prevent this struts are introduced. The stress in the struts (compression) is indicated by arrows pointing towards the joint. In page 92 (4) the complete roof structure is shown.

Page 92 (5) shows a method of trussing the roof which is most suitable for built up sections where bolts and connectors are used instead of framing joints. Page 92 (6) shows a method of trussing for large spans.

Structural members

The roof structure must be strong enough to support the weight of the roof covering, with an allowance for snow and wind pressure.

The *rafters* give direct support to the roof covering, and may be thought of as inclined beams. The size of the rafter's section varies according to the weight of the roof covering; in the case of a light covering it should be between 50×75 mm and 40×100 mm. When there is a heavy roof covering, the section should be between 50×100 mm and 63×125 mm. The standard spacing for rafters depends on the weight of the roof covering. The centres of the rafters are usually 375 to 450 mm apart.

The *wall plates* should be bedded on to the wall, preferably with a mixture of lime mortar and hair. The wall plate gives support to the feet of the rafters. The traditional section size is 75 × 115 mm and this is most convenient for brickwork, since it equals one course (75 mm) in thickness and a half brick (115 mm) in width.

The *ridge* supports the top end of the rafters and provides the link between each pair. The section size is mainly dependent on the pitch. A steeply pitched roof requires a deep ridge to accommodate the long splay-cut at the top end of the rafter. A low pitched roof may have a section 25 × 150 mm, 32 × 175 mm, or 40 × 175 mm, whereas a steeply pitched roof should have a section 25 × 175 mm, 32 × 200 mm, or 40 × 225–275 mm.

The *purlins* provide intermediate support for the rafters, and they themselves are supported at each end by a wall or truss. The length of the purlins depends on the spacing of the trusses or party walls. These are usually 3 to 4 metres apart, and must not be placed more than 5 metres apart. Span, pitch and weight of structure can all affect the size and shape of the purlins' section. A light structure may have purlins 63 × 75 mm, 75 × 150 mm, or 75 × 175 mm. A heavy structure may have purlins 75 × 225 mm, 100 × 175 mm, or 100 × 275 mm.

Roofs may be classified according to their construction; they are generally either trussed or untrussed.

Untrussed roofs include those of small span, that is of up to 5 metres, roofs on buildings with party walls, couple roofs, roofs with collar ties, ceiling joists, and so on. The trussed roofs consists of independent frames or trusses supporting the roof members. The trusses are placed at intervals of 3 to 4 metres.

Untrussed roofs

Page 93 (top) shows a couple roof suitable for spans of up to 4 metres. The purlins are supported on party walls. The second diagram shows a collar roof suitable for spans of up to 5 metres. The purlins in this case are supported by the collar ties. The height of the collar should not exceed one third the height of the roof. The third diagram shows a typical cottage roof suitable for spans of up to 8 metres.

Trussed roofs

Page 94 (top) shows a roof containing two trusses. They are shown in position, resting at each end on 450 mm piers. The type of truss used depends on the span of roof and class of building. Trusses are necessary on all roofs of this type with a clear span of over 7 metres.

Page 94 (middle) shows a *king post truss* suitable for spans of between 6 metres and 9 metres. The truss should be set out on centre lines as indicated. Mortise and tenon joints are used, and all the main joints have metal fasteners. The maximum depth of tenons is 32 mm. It is necessary to lift the struts 300 mm from the centre of the beam in order to make a satisfactory joint. The camber required on the beam is got by reducing the length of the king post by 12 mm in every 3 metre span. Framed up king post trusses are almost obsolete, having been replaced by other forms of construction.

The *built-up truss* has many advantages over the traditional framed type. It requires less timber, a simplified method of jointing can be used, and it is thus easier and quicker to make. Page 94 (foot) shows a typical built-up truss suitable for a span of 7 to 8·5 metres. No traditional methods of jointing are used for this work; the members are laid over each other, and fastened with bolts and connectors.

Trussed rafters

Much research into roof construction has been carried out by the various Institutes and Associations, and this has resulted in simplifications which make possible considerable economies in timber and labour. Page 93 (foot) is a typical example of this. Here strutting from the party walls is eliminated, and the joints in the truss are fastened with bolts and connectors.

Eaves

Three methods of finishing the eaves of a roof are shown on page 95:

First, 50 × 100 mm rafters are birdsmouthed over the wall plate, with a wrot (planed) finish at the ends. The rafters project by 300–450 mm at the eaves, and the sprockets are at least 600 mm long. The tilting fillet is 50 × 100 mm, with a wrot finish.

The second shows boxed-in eaves with fascia and soffit. The fascia is 32 mm thick and at least 175 mm deep in order that it may be fixed securely and that there should be adequate falls for the rainwater gutter. The soffit, usually 25 mm thick, is tongued into the fascia and fixed to the bearers, which are in turn fastened to the side of each rafter.

The third is a way of constructing eaves with a large overhang. The main rafters are birdsmouthed on to the wall plate, and the broken rafters, forming the eaves, are birdsmouthed over the wall plate. The wide soffit needs to be built up from narrow widths of wood tongued and grooved together.

The correct proportions of a birdsmouth joint to rafter are shown on page 95 (middle). The amount cut away should not exceed one third the width of the rafter.

Page 96 (top) gives details of the joint between the collar tie and the rafter. The joint is fastened with bolts or coach screws.

The second and third drawings show the two ways of setting purlins; at right angles to the roof slope, and at the foot of the page, in a vertical position.

Operations involved in the cutting and fixing of roof timbers

The details of the proposed roof are given in page 97. The drawings show a plan and vertical section with a scale of 1 : 50, and full-size details of the members.

Sequence of operations

1   Take accurate dimensions from the actual building.
2   Set out rafter lengths.
3   Mark out the pattern template rafters, trimming rafters, halving and scarfing joints.
4   Cut all rafters, marking each one from the pattern rafter.
5   Make all joints in the wall plates, ridge and purlins.
6   Mark out the position of the rafters on ridge and wall plates.
7   Erect and finish.

The lengths and bevels of the rafters are given on page 98 (top). The marking out of each member is also shown:

75 × 115 mm wall plates halved together and marked out for rafters
32 × 175 mm ridge scarfed together and marked out for rafters
75 × 175 mm purlins scarfed together
50 × 100 mm pattern rafters
One pair of trimming rafters
One trimmer pattern.

The diagram on page 99 (top) shows how each joint should be nailed. 75 mm and 100 mm nails are required to fasten rafters to the ridges. 125 mm and 150 mm spikes are used to fasten the rafters to the purlins, and the rafters to the wall plates. Round wire nails are extensively used for roofing; they are easy to drive and do not split the timber.

First fix three or four pairs of rafters, followed by the ridge (temporary supports may be needed for this). Next place the purlins in position, and fix the remaining rafters. Form the gutters behind the chimney stacks, and fix the fascia and soffit. The roof is now ready for felting, lathing, and slating.

Roofs of special character

Roofs are generally designed to suit a particular type of building. For civic and public buildings such as halls, places of entertainment and some educational buildings, the open decorative type of roof is most suitable; and when these buildings are traditional in design the roof trusses are usually of the framed type with a wrot (planed) surface finish to all members including the rafters, the purlins, the wall plates and the ridge. The collar beam type of truss, which has shaped ribs or metal tie rods, is a popular design for most open decorative roofs, though many of the timber roofs on ecclesiastical buildings are of the hammer-beam type and have massive timbers and ornate carvings.

The traditional framed construction, however, is gradually being replaced by various forms of laminated construction. Built-up arched ribs are now used, since these eliminate the complicated scarf jointing that used to be necessary on traditional work. Glued laminated arched and cantilever ribs, again, have replaced the traditional truss and this change has resulted in a great saving of timber. These ribs, spaced 3 to 4 metres apart, are independent of the walls, and are supported on a foundation at ground level, whereas the traditional type of truss was supported by the walls at the level of the wall plates.

Many factories, warehouses and similar buildings have roofs of 15 to 30 metre span, and these can be classified as large-span buildings. The traditional type of framed truss for large-span roofs used to be the combined queen and princess post or the composite truss. Both these types of truss have now become obsolete.

The bowstring, or Belfast truss, is commonly used for factory and storage buildings. The truss consists of a curved bow, a built-up beam, and struts which are arranged in lattice formation. No framing joints are used but all the members must be securely nailed together. Spans extending to 36 metres are possible with this type of truss, but the most economical span is one of 15 metres. The latest forms of truss for large-span buildings are no longer nailed together, however. It is becoming customary to use bowstring trusses in laminated form, or lattice girder-type trusses. These are sandwich-like in construction, and their joints are secured with timber connectors. With these improved methods larger spans, from 45 to 60 metres, can be achieved.

Only a brief description of these roofs is given in this volume, but the subject will be dealt with in greater detail in Book 2.

NOTE The geometry of the hipped roof is dealt with in the chapter on workshop geometry. Its construction and erection will be described in Book 2.

Practice lessons

1 Working from the information given on pages 91–92:

   (a) Draw diagrams to prove the efficiency of a triangular shaped construction and its application to roof construction.

   (b) Make neat diagrams to show the nature of the stresses in the members of a king post truss.

   (c) Make neat diagrams to show the difference between untrussed roofs, trussed roofs, and trussed rafters.

2 *(a)* Draw the plan and sectional view of the couple roof as shown on page 97. Scale 1:50.

   (b) Make 1:5 scale details of the eaves, wall plate, purlin and ridge. Give the section size of each member.

   (c) Make neat diagrams to show how the wall plates, the purlins, and the ridge are jointed together in their length.

3 *(a)* Make neat drawings to explain the following roofing terms.
   - (i)   Tilting fillet
   - (ii) Sprocket piece
   - (iii) Broken rafters
   - (iv) Fascia and soffit
   - (v)   Birdsmouth

ROOFS
CLASSIFICATION ACCORDING TO SHAPE

FLAT ROOFS

LEAN TO ROOFS

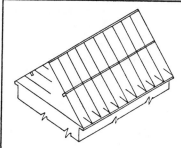

COUPLE ROOFS

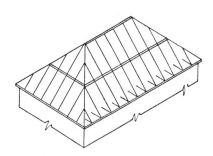

HIPPED ROOFS

ROOFS
ROOF COVERINGS

FLAT ROOFS

SUITABLE COVERING
ASPHALT
LEAD
COPPER

10° TO 20° PITCH

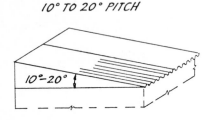

10°-20°

SUITABLE COVERING
LARGE CORRUGATED
SHEETS
LARGE ALUMINIUM
SHEETS
LARGE ASBESTOS
SHEETS

30° TO 35° PITCH

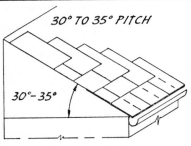

30°-35°

SUITABLE COVERING
LARGE SLATES
ASBESTOS SLATES
SHINGLES
HARDBOARD SLATES

40° TO 60° PITCH

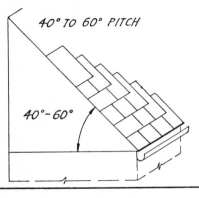

40°-60°

SUITABLE COVERING
SMALL SLATES
PLAIN TILES
STONE SLATES

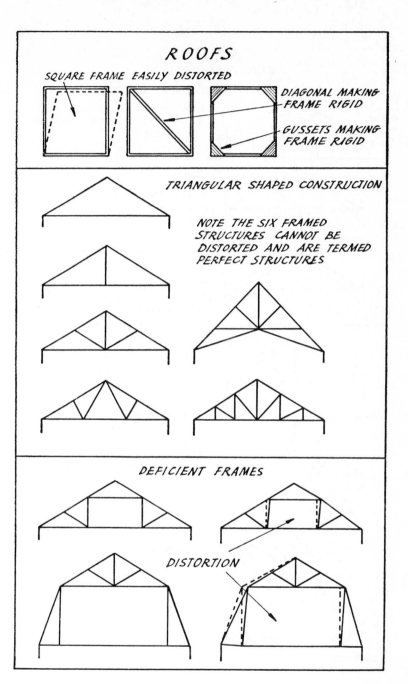

ROOFS

SQUARE FRAME EASILY DISTORTED

DIAGONAL MAKING FRAME RIGID

GUSSETS MAKING FRAME RIGID

TRIANGULAR SHAPED CONSTRUCTION

NOTE THE SIX FRAMED STRUCTURES CANNOT BE DISTORTED AND ARE TERMED PERFECT STRUCTURES

DEFICIENT FRAMES

DISTORTION

ROOFS
STRUCTURAL DESIGN

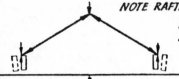

NOTE RAFTERS TEND TO SPREAD WALLS

COMPRESSION STRESS INDICATED
BY ARROWS POINTING TOWARDS
THE JOINT

TIE INTRODUCED TO PREVENT
SPREADING

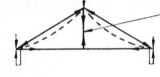

KING ROD OR POST INTRODUCED
TO PREVENT DEFLECTION IN TIE

TENSILE STRESS INDICATED BY
ARROWS POINTING TOWARDS
THE CENTRE

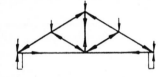

KING POST TRUSS

STRUTS INTRODUCED TO
PREVENT BENDING IN RAFTERS

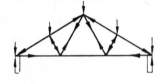

METHOD OF TRUSSING
MOST SUITABLE FOR
BUILT UP STRUCTURES

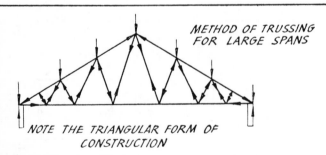

METHOD OF TRUSSING
FOR LARGE SPANS

NOTE THE TRIANGULAR FORM OF
CONSTRUCTION

ROOFS

UNTRUSSED ROOFS

COUPLE ROOF

SUITABLE FOR SPANS
OF UP TO 4 METRES

COLLAR ROOF

NOTE HEIGHT OF COLLAR
1/3 RD HEIGHT OF ROOF

COTTAGE TYPE ROOF

SUITABLE FOR SPANS
OF UP TO 8 METRES

TRUSSED RAFTERS

NOTE STRUTTING FROM
THE PARTY WALLS
IS ELIMINATED

ROOFS
TRUSSED ROOFS

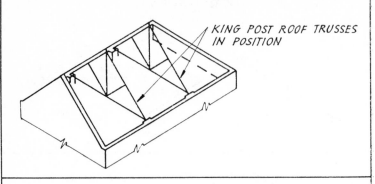

KING POST ROOF TRUSSES
IN POSITION

TYPICAL KING POST ROOF TRUSS

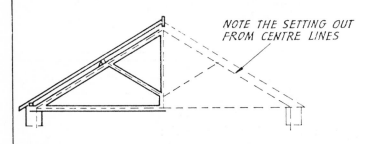

NOTE THE SETTING OUT
FROM CENTRE LINES

TYPICAL BUILT UP TRUSS

SUITABLE FOR SPANS 5·7 TO 8 METRES

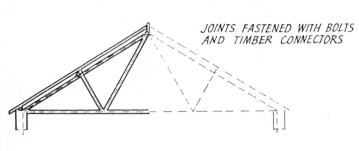

JOINTS FASTENED WITH BOLTS
AND TIMBER CONNECTORS

ROOFS

CONSTRUCTIONAL DETAILS
FINISHINGS AT EAVES

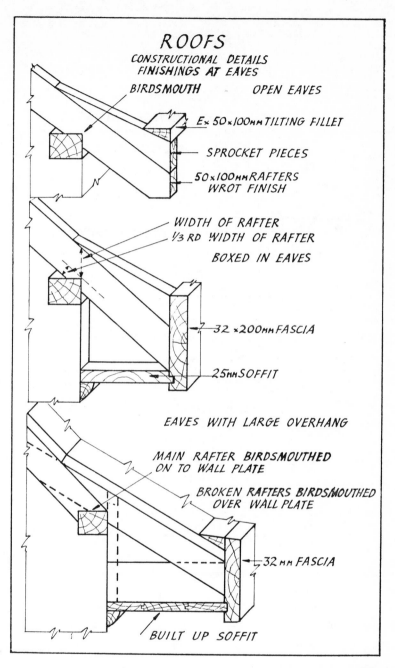

BIRDSMOUTH — OPEN EAVES

Ex 50×100mm TILTING FILLET

SPROCKET PIECES

50×100mm RAFTERS
WROT FINISH

WIDTH OF RAFTER
⅓ RD WIDTH OF RAFTER

BOXED IN EAVES

32×200mm FASCIA

25mm SOFFIT

EAVES WITH LARGE OVERHANG

MAIN RAFTER BIRDSMOUTHED
ON TO WALL PLATE

BROKEN RAFTERS BIRDSMOUTHED
OVER WALL PLATE

32mm FASCIA

BUILT UP SOFFIT

95

ROOFS
CONSTRUCTIONAL DETAILS

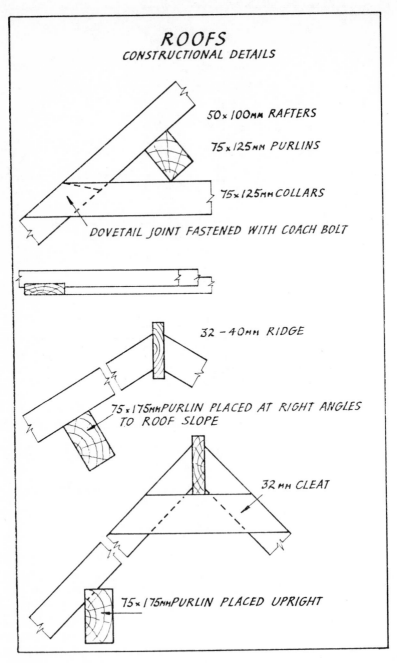

50 x 100mm RAFTERS

75 x 125mm PURLINS

75 x 125mm COLLARS

DOVETAIL JOINT FASTENED WITH COACH BOLT

32 – 40mm RIDGE

75 x 175mm PURLIN PLACED AT RIGHT ANGLES TO ROOF SLOPE

32 mm CLEAT

75 x 175mm PURLIN PLACED UPRIGHT

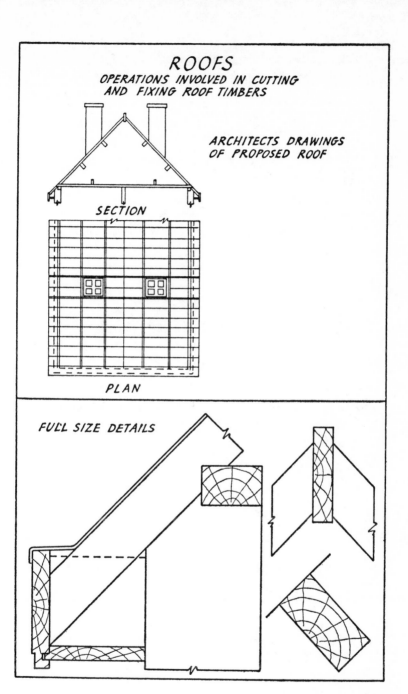

ROOFS
OPERATIONS INVOLVED IN CUTTING
AND FIXING ROOF TIMBERS

ARCHITECTS DRAWINGS
OF PROPOSED ROOF

SECTION

PLAN

FULL SIZE DETAILS

97

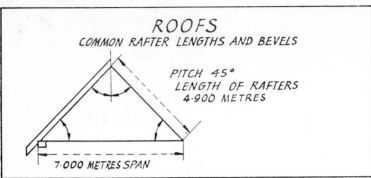

ROOFS
COMMON RAFTER LENGTHS AND BEVELS

PITCH 45°
LENGTH OF RAFTERS
4·900 METRES

7·000 METRES SPAN

METHOD OF MARKING OUT AND CUTTING EACH MEMBER

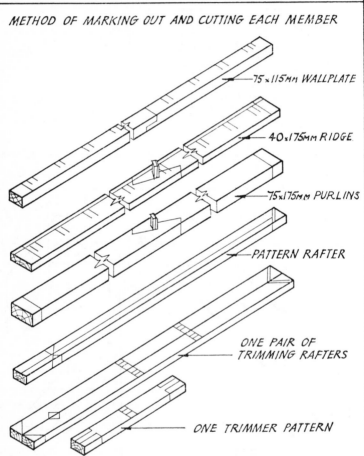

75 × 115MM WALLPLATE

40 × 175MM RIDGE

75 × 175MM PURLINS

PATTERN RAFTER

ONE PAIR OF
TRIMMING RAFTERS

ONE TRIMMER PATTERN

ROOFS
METHOD OF NAILING

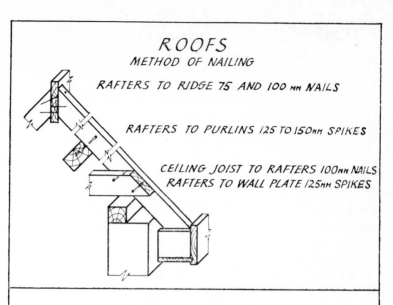

RAFTERS TO RIDGE 75 AND 100 mm NAILS

RAFTERS TO PURLINS 125 TO 150mm SPIKES

CEILING JOIST TO RAFTERS 100mm NAILS
RAFTERS TO WALL PLATE 125mm SPIKES

METHOD OF ERECTION

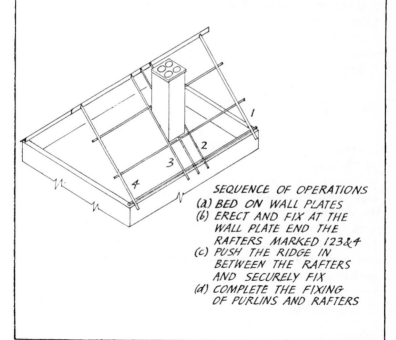

SEQUENCE OF OPERATIONS
(a) BED ON WALL PLATES
(b) ERECT AND FIX AT THE
WALL PLATE END THE
RAFTERS MARKED 123&4
(c) PUSH THE RIDGE IN
BETWEEN THE RAFTERS
AND SECURELY FIX
(d) COMPLETE THE FIXING
OF PURLINS AND RAFTERS

8 | Formwork

Formwork is temporary work used in casting reinforced concrete structures. It may be required for lintels, beams, floor slabs, columns, and stairs.

Formwork is constructed mainly from timber and steel. It must be strong enough to support wet concrete, which may weigh from 2,000 to 3,000 kilograms per cubic metre. It must also remain rigid while the concrete is consolidated by ramming, tamping, or vibration. It is essential that joints should be tight-fitting to prevent the escape of the liquid concrete.

All formwork must be designed to allow for its easy and gradual removal after the concrete has hardened. This operation is called striking.

Shuttering to beams and lintels

Small concrete lintels over single door openings are generally pre-cast and placed into position as one unit, but the larger lintels are best cast *in situ*.

The formwork for casting a lintel *in situ* is illustrated on page 104. Elevation and section views are given which show the props, struts, and easing wedges. An enlarged isometric view of the form-work is shown in the middle of the page, with details of the beam casing made up of 25–32 mm tongued-and-grooved boards. Notice the brackets screwed to the bearers, and the stretcher to prevent spreading in the middle. A section and side view of the formwork is given at the foot of page 104 which shows in detail the bracket, easing wedges, and props. As much as possible of the work should be prefabricated.

All the timbers, with the exception of the props, should ideally

be wrot finished (planed). When a smooth finish to the concrete
is required, the casing should be lined with hardboard, plywood,
plastic, or metal sheeting.

Formwork to floors

The plan and vertical section view of a reinforced concrete floor
are given on page 105.

The formwork required consists of a platform to support the
150 mm floor slab, and beam casings to support the two main
beams. The floor slab decking is formed of 32 mm jointed boards
supported by 63 × 150 mm joists placed at 600 mm centres. The
beam casing has 32 mm cleated sides, and 40 to 50 mm thick soffit
boards. The joists and beam casings are supported on props placed
at intervals of 900 to 1,200 mm. Provision for easing and striking
is made by placing folding wedges between the bottom end of the
prop and the sole piece. The sole piece is a timber plate.

NOTE   It is usual on large reinforced concrete jobs to use adjustable metal props.

The constructional details at the foot of page 105 show the
formwork from below. Notice the spacing and the position of the
props supporting the joists and beam casings.

The enlarged details given on page 106 (top) show the head of
a prop, which consists of a post, a head tree, and braces. The prop
gives direct support to the 75 × 175 mm runner. The runner
takes the ends of the decking joists which support the decking
boards.

A prop under a main beam is shown in the middle of page 106.
Notice that the props give support not only to the main beam, but
also the ends of the joists supporting the floor slab. Details are also
given of the folding wedges and the sole piece.

It is usual to connect or tie the props together so that less timber
is used. This is illustrated at the foot of page 106. The props,
which are spaced at 1,200 mm centres, are shown connected in the
middle by 25 × 75 mm ties. A line of ties is also placed at the
bottom of the props to prevent any movement of the formwork.

Surface finish

The surface finish to formwork depends on the standard of surface finish required for the concrete. When the concrete is to be plastered or covered with other materials, then the formwork is best made with rough-sawn boards to give a coarse 'key', but softwood boards of wrot finish can be used. When a high standard of surface finish is required, smooth, non-porous facing materials should be used. Exterior plywoods, tempered hardboards, plastic and metal sheets are then most suitable.

Constructional details for the various types of boards are shown on page 107.

Two ways of jointing the wrot boards are shown at the top of page 107. Notice the special vee joint which allows for expansion of the boards. The use of 9 mm exterior plywood supported on 25 × 150 mm boards is illustrated in the third drawing.

The facing of a beam and floor-slab decking using tempered hardboard are illustrated in the middle of page 107. Hardwood fillets form the rounded corners. The use of wrot boards to give a satisfactory finish on a concrete steel frame building is shown at the foot of page 107. This formwork is supported on hangers from the main steel beams, instead of by propping from the floor below.

Since external angles are difficult to realise in concrete work, hollow, rounded, or splayed fillets are used. Rounded or splayed fillets are also incorporated to form shaped internal angles to make the striking of the formwork easier.

Materials

European redwood of third or fourth quality is extensively used for formwork, but Douglas fir and pitch pine are sometimes employed when heavy loads have to be supported.

It is an advantage to standardise the size of formwork units so that they can be used again, since this will greatly reduce building costs. Before re-use, the timber should be cleaned and brushed over with whitewash or soft soap.

Practice lessons

1 Working from the information given:

   (a) Draw the elevation and sectional view of a door opening as shown on page 104.

   (b) Show, on the drawing, the formwork required to form the cast *in situ* lintel.

   (c) Make an isometric view of the formwork required to cast the lintel.

   (d) Draw, to a 1:5 scale, a section and side view of the formwork.

2 *(a)* Draw the plan and vertical section of the reinforced concrete floor as shown on page 105. Scale 1:50.

   (b) Add to the drawing the formwork and props required.

   (c) Make 1:5 scale details of the main beam formwork and propping system.

3 *(a)* Make neat diagrams of the shuttering materials, in common use, as illustrated on page 107.

   (b) Explain the functions and necessity for:
     (i) Folding wedges
     (ii) Adjustable props
     (iii) Shutter oil or soap.

FORMWORK

SHUTTERING TO BEAMS

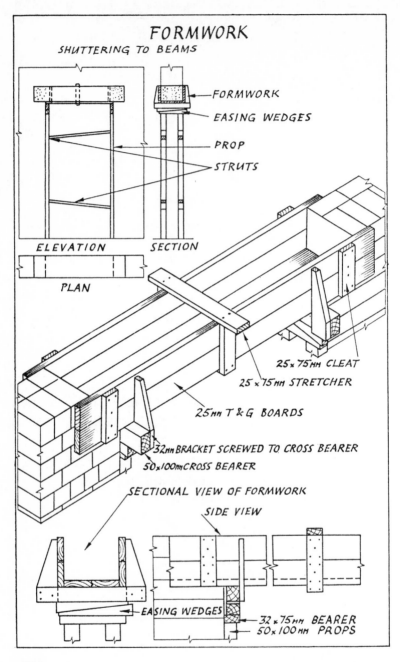

FORMWORK

EASING WEDGES

PROP

STRUTS

ELEVATION   SECTION

PLAN

25 x 75mm CLEAT

25 x 75mm STRETCHER

25mm T & G BOARDS

32mm BRACKET SCREWED TO CROSS BEARER

50 x 100mm CROSS BEARER

SECTIONAL VIEW OF FORMWORK

SIDE VIEW

EASING WEDGES

32 x 75mm BEARER

50 x 100mm PROPS

FORMWORK

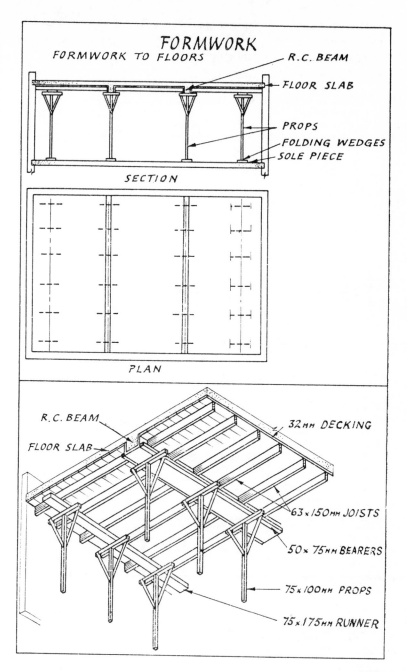

FORMWORK TO FLOORS

R.C. BEAM

FLOOR SLAB

PROPS

FOLDING WEDGES

SOLE PIECE

SECTION

PLAN

R.C. BEAM

FLOOR SLAB

32 mm DECKING

63 × 150 mm JOISTS

50 × 75 mm BEARERS

75 × 100 mm PROPS

75 × 175 mm RUNNER

FORMWORK

CONSTRUCTIONAL DETAILS

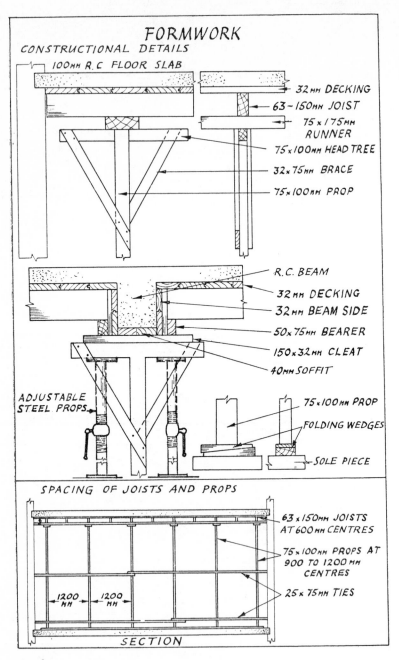

100ᴍᴍ R.C FLOOR SLAB

32 ᴍᴍ DECKING

63–150ᴍᴍ JOIST

75 × 175ᴍᴍ RUNNER

75 × 100ᴍᴍ HEAD TREE

32 × 75ᴍᴍ BRACE

75 × 100ᴍᴍ PROP

R.C. BEAM

32 ᴍᴍ DECKING

32 ᴍᴍ BEAM SIDE

50 × 75ᴍᴍ BEARER

150 × 32ᴍᴍ CLEAT

40ᴍᴍ SOFFIT

ADJUSTABLE STEEL PROPS.

75 × 100ᴍᴍ PROP

FOLDING WEDGES

SOLE PIECE

SPACING OF JOISTS AND PROPS

63 × 150ᴍᴍ JOISTS AT 600 ᴍᴍ CENTRES

75 × 100ᴍᴍ PROPS AT 900 TO 1200 ᴍᴍ CENTRES

25 × 75ᴍᴍ TIES

1200 ᴍᴍ 1200 ᴍᴍ

SECTION

FORMWORK

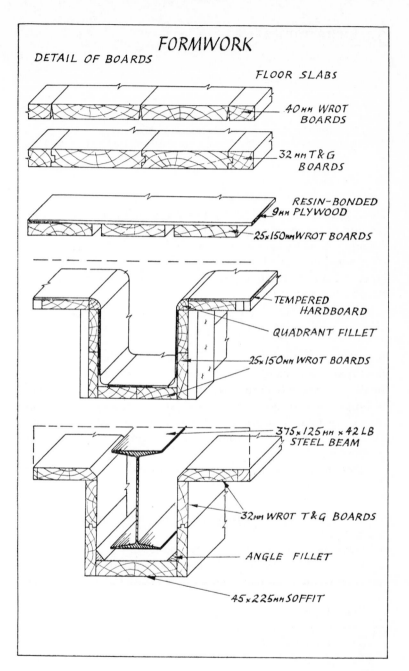

DETAIL OF BOARDS

FLOOR SLABS

40 mm WROT BOARDS

32 mm T&G BOARDS

RESIN-BONDED 9 mm PLYWOOD

25 x 150 mm WROT BOARDS

TEMPERED HARDBOARD

QUADRANT FILLET

25 x 150 mm WROT BOARDS

375 x 125 mm x 42 LB STEEL BEAM

32 mm WROT T&G BOARDS

ANGLE FILLET

45 x 225 mm SOFFIT

Door frames are required to provide a fixing for doors. The sections of the members, especially the jambs on which the doors are hung, must be large enough to enable the frame to remain rigid even when only fixed at the head and foot of each jamb. This, however, is not usually done, and door frames generally are also fixed in the middle.

Classification of door frames

Door frames can be classified as internal or external. The internal door frames are mainly in the form of casings. The members are smaller in section than those of the external frames, and fixing has to be provided in the centre of the jambs. External door frames may be further classified into two groups: ordinary door frames for doors opening inwards and outwards; and combined door and window frames.

Combined door and window frames include wing door frames (usually opening inwards), french windows (usually opening outwards) and vestibule frames (usually opening inwards).

The four types of door frames in common use are illustrated on page 113:
1   Door frame consisting of jambs and head.
2   Door frame consisting of jambs, head and threshold.
3   Door frame, with fixed fanlight, consisting of jambs, head and transom.
4   Door frame, with hung fanlight, consisting of jambs, head, transom, threshold and fanlight.

Notice the enlarged sections of the thresholds and transoms.

Combined window and door frames are extensively used in

domestic work. The doors usually open inwards and the casements outwards. A typical combined frame is illustrated on page 114 (top), with enlarged details of the mullion and casement stile.

French windows not only let in light and air; they also give access on to a verandah or porch. In Great Britain many french windows open outwards, but the original french windows used on the Continent open inwards, and lead on to a small balcony. The illustrations on page 114 (foot) show a frame opening outwards with enlarged details of the head and threshold.

Vestibule frames may have doors opening inwards or double swing doors, though the latter are mainly used in public buildings. A typical vestibule frame for domestic work is illustrated on page 115 (top), together with enlarged details of the threshold and side lights. A vestibule frame of modern design with enlarged details is also shown on page 115 (foot).

Design of sections

When designing the section shape of the members, particular attention must be paid to the shape of the thresholds and transoms in order to make sure that driving rain will not be able to penetrate the building. It is usual to insert metal water bars in the threshold, but it is more difficult to make casements and doors opening inwards weatherproof, particularly at the corners.

The members' section size must be related to the weight and size of the door they have to carry. The sizes in common use are:
50×100 mm (light doors up to $2,000 \times 800$ mm).
63×100 mm, 75×115 mm (all types of doors up to $2,000 \times 800$ mm).
75×150 mm, 100×175 mm (large doors up to $2,300 \times 3,000$ mm).

Methods of jointing

The joint most commonly used in frames is the mortise and tenon. Three methods of securing it have been developed, and these are illustrated on page 116:
1 Draw pinning
2 Wedging and pinning
3 Nailing.

Draw pinning has the advantage that the joint can be pulled up without the use of cramps. It is, however, unsuitable for modern methods of production.

The *wedging and pinning* method is now extensively used, since it is ideal for the production of door frames on a large scale. The joints may be glued and pinned, or glued and then wedged. In low cost work only the pins and wedges are glued.

The *nailing* of joints is not much done nowadays, but it was common practice in general joinery work during the years between the wars.

Operations involved in the making of door frames, excluding the cutting out and planing

Two door frames have been taken as examples, and drawings and details of these appear on page 117. The sequence of operations is as follows:

1   Set out the height and width rod. The rod is shown set out on page 118 (top). Two views are given of the width rod, one above the transom and one below.

2   Prepare the cutting list, which should be in triplicate and provide two columns for office use. It is essential as a record of the timber needed, and also of the timber used. This information is wanted for purposes of costing. On the list should appear the name of the member, its cutting size and finished size. The kind of wood used should also be stated. This is a typical cutting list:

Member	No.	Cutting size (millimetres)	Finished size (mm)	Material
Jambs	2	2,500×75×100	72×97	European redwood
Head	1	1,100×75×100	72×97	,,
Jambs	2	2,550×75×100	72×97	
Head	1	1,100×75×100	72×97	,,
Transom	1	1,000×75×150	72×150	,,
Beads	2	900×14×50	12×47	,,
Beads	2	350×14×50	12×47	,,

3 Cut out material.
4 Plane to size.
5 Mark out for joints. Special care must be taken in the marking
out of the shoulders (see page 118).

NOTE All jambs must be set out in pairs. Start marking out on
the face edge, taking the overall sizes first. Use great care when
setting up the mortise gauge.

6 Mortise two heads and one pair of jambs, and rip tenons on
two pairs of jambs and one transom.
7 Prepare the rebates and moulding. When large rebates are
being worked by hand, the waste from them can partly be removed
by ploughing.
8 Shoulder cut and scribe. This should be done with special care.
Each jamb should be scribed.
9 Clean up the inside edges. In the case of large framing, such
as the example dealt with here, clean up all visible faces.
10 Knock together and finish off. When they are made of
hardwood, each joint of the frame should be fitted separately. This
process is called fitting up.
11 Fit in beads and finishing.

NOTE Each process should be completely finished before the
next is started.

   In order that the frame should be kept rigid and square during
building operations, all ordinary door frames need bracing with
squaring strips. The strips, which are about 18 × 50 mm, are cut
into the rebates. The proper way of assembling door frames,
illustrated on page 119 (top), is as follows:
   (i)   Place the frame, rebate side up, on the bench.
   (ii)   Nail the stretcher (18 × 50 mm) into the rebate.
   (iii) Cramp the jambs and test for square from corner to corner.
   (iv)   With the cramp still in position, fasten the joints.
   (v)   Cut and nail in the squaring strips.
   (vi)   Clean off the frame on both sides.
   (vii) Cut in glazing beads to the fanlight of the frame as shown
on page 119 (foot).

Practice lessons

1 Working from the information given:

    (a) Prepare a plan and elevation view of a single door frame with transom as illustrated on page 117. Scale 1:20.

    (b) Draw 1:5 scale details of the jambs, head and transom.

2 Make neat sketches of the following methods of jointing:

    (a) Draw pinning

    (b) Wedging and pinning.

3 Working from the instructions given:

    (a) Set out a workshop rod for the door frame as shown on page 117.

    (b) Carry out all the operations involved in making the frame.

DOOR FRAMES

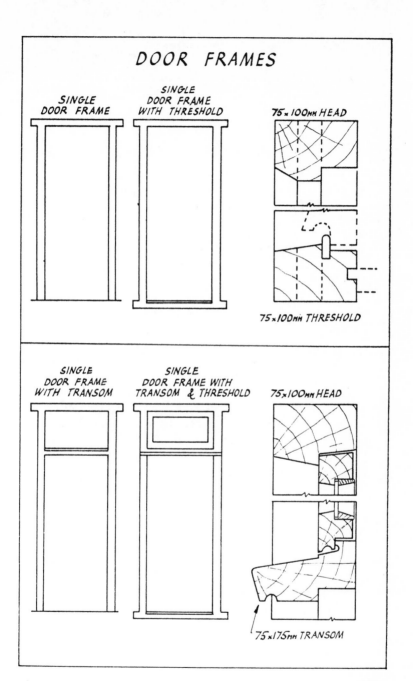

SINGLE DOOR FRAME

SINGLE DOOR FRAME WITH THRESHOLD

75 x 100mm HEAD

75 x 100mm THRESHOLD

SINGLE DOOR FRAME WITH TRANSOM

SINGLE DOOR FRAME WITH TRANSOM & THRESHOLD

75 x 100mm HEAD

75 x 175mm TRANSOM

DOOR FRAMES
COMBINED FRAMES

SINGLE WING FRAME WITH THRESHOLD

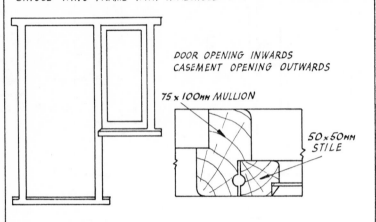

DOOR OPENING INWARDS
CASEMENT OPENING OUTWARDS

75 x 100mm MULLION

50 x 50mm STILE

FRENCH WINDOWS

DOOR AND CASEMENTS OPENING OUTWARDS

75 x 100mm HEAD

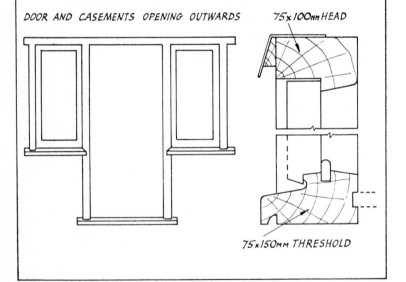

75 x 150mm THRESHOLD

DOOR FRAMES

VESTIBULE FRAME WITH DOOR OPENING INWARDS

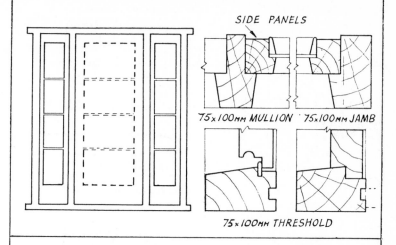

SIDE PANELS

75×100mm MULLION   75×100mm JAMB

75×100mm THRESHOLD

VESTIBULE FRAME WITH DOUBLE SWING DOORS

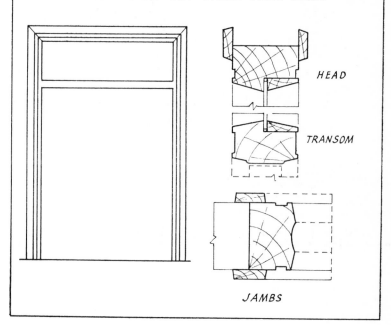

HEAD

TRANSOM

JAMBS

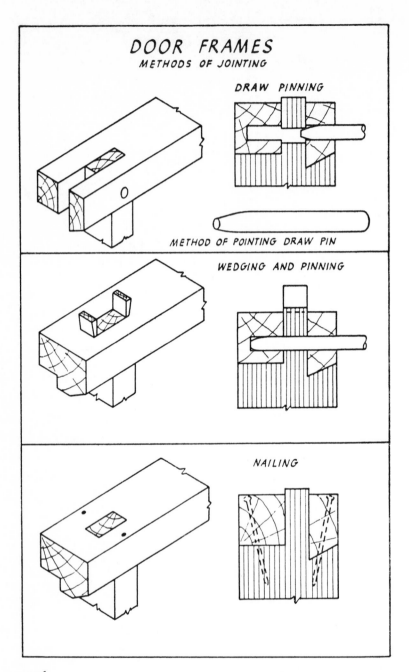

DOOR FRAMES
METHODS OF JOINTING

DRAW PINNING

METHOD OF POINTING DRAW PIN

WEDGING AND PINNING

NAILING

DOOR FRAMES
OPERATIONS INVOLVED IN MAKING DOOR FRAMES
ARCHITECTS DRAWINGS AND DETAILS

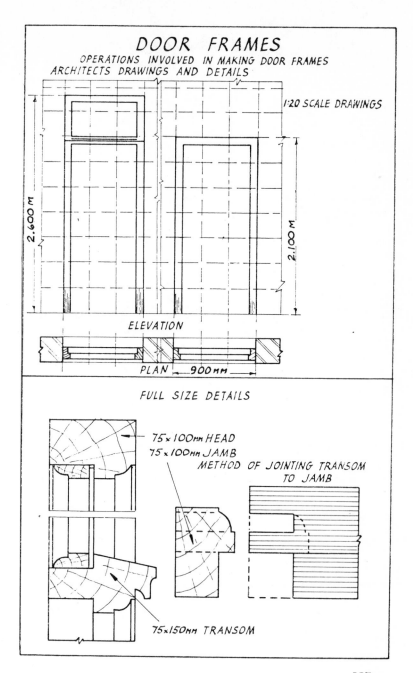

1:20 SCALE DRAWINGS

2.600 M

2.100 M

ELEVATION

PLAN ⌐ 900 MM ⌐

FULL SIZE DETAILS

75 × 100 MM HEAD

75 × 100 MM JAMB

METHOD OF JOINTING TRANSOM
TO JAMB

75 × 150 MM TRANSOM

DOOR FRAMES

OPERATIONS INVOLVED IN MAKING DOOR FRAMES
HEIGHT AND WIDTH ROD

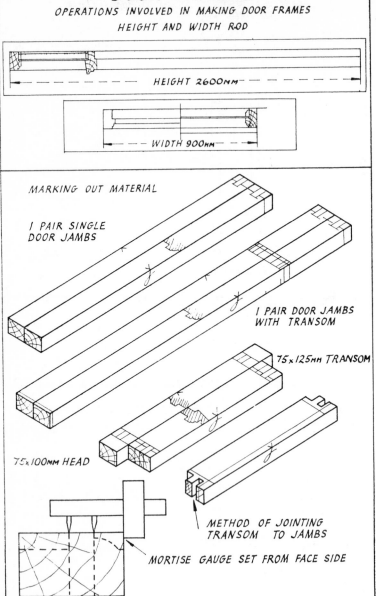

HEIGHT 2600MM

WIDTH 900MM

MARKING OUT MATERIAL

I PAIR SINGLE
DOOR JAMBS

I PAIR DOOR JAMBS
WITH TRANSOM

75 x 125MM TRANSOM

75 x 100MM HEAD

METHOD OF JOINTING
TRANSOM TO JAMBS

MORTISE GAUGE SET FROM FACE SIDE

DOOR FRAMES
OPERATIONS INVOLVED IN MAKING DOOR FRAMES

ASSEMBLY OF SINGLE DOOR FRAME
DETAIL OF SQUARING ROD

SQUARING STRIPS

NOTE FOR A PERFECT SQUARE
THE DIAGONALS MUST BE EQUAL

ASSEMBLY OF DOOR FRAME WITH TRANSOM

NOTE NO SQUARING STRIPS
ARE REQUIRED

Like door frames, doors can best be classified as external or internal. The external doors include the front entrance, back entrance and french windows. Internal doors include entrance doors to rooms, swing doors, and vestibule doors.

A door opening must be large enough for people to be able to walk through with ease, and to allow the passage of goods and equipment. Entrance doors are usually slightly bigger than internal doors.

The British Standards Institution recommend that the overall size of all components should be multiples of a 300 mm module. This means that the door size is controlled by the size of the frame and dispenses with the present practice of making frames to suit standard size doors.

During the transitional period from imperial to metric measure standard doors, of imperial size, will be required on a wide range of repair and reconstruction work. Four standard doors are illustrated at the top of page 126. Notice that the imperial size, and the metric equivalent, is given.

The recommended width of a single door opening is 900 mm and the height 2,100 mm. This gives a door size of 800 mm wide by 2,050 mm high (equivalent imperial size, 2 ft $7\frac{1}{2}$ in wide by 6 ft $8\frac{3}{4}$ in high).

Standard sizes of doors

A single door, and two pairs of doors, set out on a 300 mm planning grid, are illustrated on page 126, with a full size section of the frame and door stile at the foot of the page.

Notice that this one standard size for a single door could replace 75% of the varied door sizes in common use today.

EXTERNAL DOORS

Ledged and braced doors consist of boards tongued and grooved together, with ledges and braces added on the reverse side. The boards should be 25 mm thick, and not more than 125 mm wide. The ledges should be 32 × 150 mm, and the braces 32 × 100 mm.

A typical ledged and braced door is illustrated on page 127 (top), with enlarged details of boards and ledges.

Framed ledged and braced doors consist of an outer frame with a sheeting of tongue and groove match-boards. The frame consists of 100 mm stiles and top rail, 225 mm middle and bottom rails. The frame is mortised and tenoned together with barefaced tenons on the middle and bottom rails. A typical framed ledged and braced door is shown on page 127 (middle), with enlarged details of boards, stile and barefaced rails.

Bead and butt panelled doors are flush panel doors used mainly for rear entrances. The panels, 25 to 32 mm thick, are tongued into the framing with a 16 mm bead on each vertical edge. A typical bead and butt panel door is shown on page 127 (foot).

Panelled doors consist of a frame made up of stiles, rails and muntins, with panels grooved into the framing. Usually the frieze panels are glazed, and the framing moulded on the solid. A typical panelled entrance door with enlarged details is shown on page 128 (top).

The top half of a *half glass door* is glazed and the lower half panelled. It is usual for this type of door to have diminished stiles, thus giving a greater glass area. A typical half glass door is illustrated on page 128 (middle) with enlarged details of panels and bars.

Fully glazed doors are used mainly for french windows and vestibule frames. The door may be putty glazed, or glazed with beads. It is illustrated on page 128 (foot), together with enlarged details of stiles and bars.

INTERNAL DOORS

A large percentage of internal doors are now factory made, and designs have been developed to suit modern trends in architecture and production. Three types of doors are illustrated on page 129.

The first, a *four panelled door*, is suitable for production by any up-to-date woodworking plant. The second, also a four panelled door, is suitable for production by a specialised plant, while the third, a *flush door*, is suitable for production by both general and specialised woodworking plants.

Methods of jointing

Three methods of joint construction have been developed:

1 Mortise and tenon
2 Dowelled
3 Laminated.

The *mortise, tenon and wedged* construction is used extensively for internal and external doors, and is a good, sound method if the wedges can be driven up to the shoulder, see page 130 (top).

The *dowelled* construction is more suitable for large scale and specialised production. The joints between the stiles and rails are dowelled, as shown page 130 (foot). The main advantage of this is the saving in timber, which amounts to approximately 225 mm on every rail. Most of the timber used in the manufacture of dowelled doors is rift sawn, and the doors are guaranteed not to twist.

The flush door is best made by a *lamintaed* construction with the two outside skins glued to a core, either solid or hollow. Both forms of construction are illustrated on page 131.

Operations involved in the making of doors

The two methods of construction which concern the joiner working in a general shop are the ledged and braced construction and the framed and panelled construction. Methodical working is essential, and to illustrate this two actual jobs using present day methods of production have been dealt with.

I   The materials—boards, ledges and braces—for the ledged and braced door would be worked to section and available in random lengths. The architect's drawings and details are shown on page 132.

Sequence of operations

These are illustrated on page 133.
1   From the drawings, set out the rod and cut off the material to length.
2   Make an assembly jig with the position of the ledges marked.
3   Place the boards face down in the jig, screw on the ledges, and fix the braces.
4   Turn the door over and nail. Three to five nails are required in each board.

NOTE   The nailing must be carefully done through the face of the boards, and neatly clinched on the back of the ledges.
In good class work the tongues and grooves are painted. It is, in fact, a good plan to prime all the members before assembly.

II   Ten four panelled doors are to be made to the drawing and details shown on pages 134 and 135.
The measurements of the door are $2,000 \times 800 \times 50$ mm. The stiles and top rails are 50×115 mm, the bottom and middle rails 50×225 mm, and the plywood panels 12 mm.

Sequence of operations

NOTE   It is assumed that the sawing, planing and mortising operations are carried out by machine.

1   Set out the height and width rod as shown on page 136 (top).
2   Prepare a cutting list (see page 124).
3   Cut out the materials taking, say, 50×115 mm stiles out of 50×225 mm wood.
4   Plane to size.

NOTE   Care must be taken in stacking to prevent the wood from twisting (see page 136—middle).

5   Mark out the material. This operation must be carefully done. The illustration (page 136—foot) shows the members for one door

Member	No.	Cutting size (mm)	Finished size (mm)	Timber
Stiles H	20	2,050 × 50 × 115	47 × 112	Redwood
Top rails	10	850 × 50 × 115	47 × 112	,,
Middle rails	10	850 × 50 × 225	47 × 222	,,
Bottom rails	10	850 × 50 × 225	47 × 222	,,
Muntins	10	1,000 × 50 × 175	47 × 112	,,
Panels	20	900 × 275 × 12		Plywood
Panels	20	600 × 275 × 12		,,

only. If made by machine only one pattern rail is needed, but it is usual to mark out all the stiles for mortising.

6   Mortise and tenon.

NOTE   If this is done by hand the tenons should only be ripped.

7   Groove (moulding on rails only).
8   Cut the shoulder (if tenons cut by hand).
9   Clean up edges and scribe muntins.
10   Cut panels to size and clean up.
11   Haunch rails as shown on page 137 (top).
12   Knock together as shown on page 137 (foot) starting with bottom rail in vice marked A and ending with stile marked B.
13   Wedge up. Place the door on the bench, face down. Glue the joints, putting plenty of glue on the shoulders and haunchings.
14   Cramp up and drive the wedges. See page 138 (top).
15   Clean off:
  (i)   Fasten door on bench as shown on page 138 (foot).
  (ii)   Level the shoulders with the jack plane.
  (iii)   Level with the trying plane, planing the muntins first, then the rails, and last the stiles.
  (iv)   Finish with the smoothing plane. Sandpaper with care, avoiding crossing the joints. Sandpaper with the grain on stained and polished work.

Practice lessons

1   Working from the information given:

   (a) To a 1:20 scale, draw the elevation view of:
      (i)   A framed and sheeted door
      (ii) A bead and butt door
      (iii) A fully glazed door.
   (b) Draw 1:5 scale details of the stiles, sheeting, panels and bar.

2   *(a)* Make isometric drawings to show the following forms of door construction:
      (i)   Mortise, tenon and wedged construction
      (ii) Dowelled construction
      (iii) Laminated construction.

3   Working from the instructions given:

   (a) Set out a workshop rod for the four panelled door and casing illustrated on page 134.
   (b) Carry out all the operations involved in making the door up to the wedging up stage.
   (c) Wedge up and clean off the door on both sides.
   (d) Fit and hang the door into a prepared opening.
   (e) Fit and fix the door furniture.

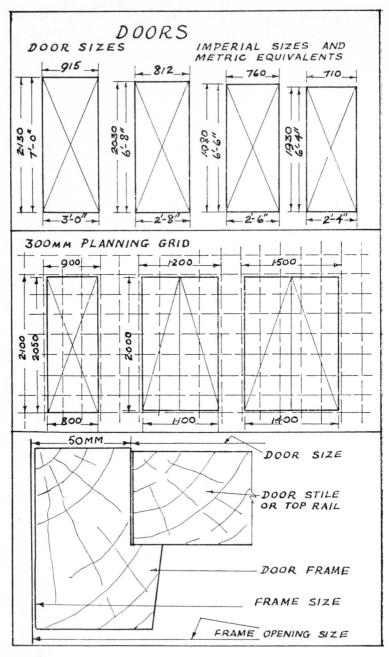

DOORS

DOOR SIZES

IMPERIAL SIZES AND METRIC EQUIVALENTS

915   812   760   710

2130 / 7'-0"   2030 / 6'-8"   1980 / 6'-6"   1930 / 6'-4"

3'-0"   2'-8"   2'-6"   2'-4"

300MM PLANNING GRID

900   1200   1500

2100 / 2050   2000

800   1100   1400

50MM

DOOR SIZE

DOOR STILE OR TOP RAIL

DOOR FRAME

FRAME SIZE

FRAME OPENING SIZE

126

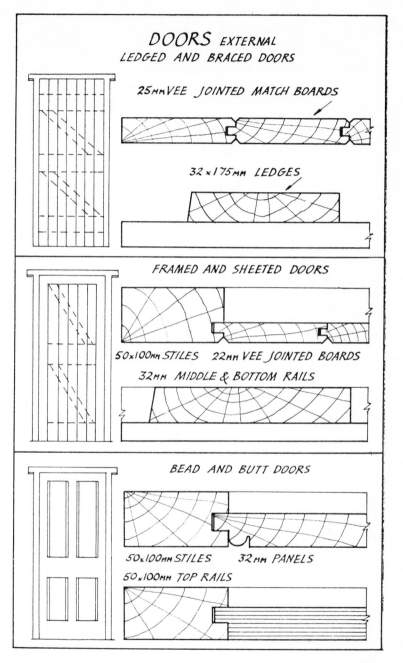

DOORS EXTERNAL
LEDGED AND BRACED DOORS

25mm VEE JOINTED MATCH BOARDS

32 x 175mm LEDGES

FRAMED AND SHEETED DOORS

50x100mm STILES   22mm VEE JOINTED BOARDS

32mm MIDDLE & BOTTOM RAILS

BEAD AND BUTT DOORS

50x100mm STILES   32mm PANELS

50x100mm TOP RAILS

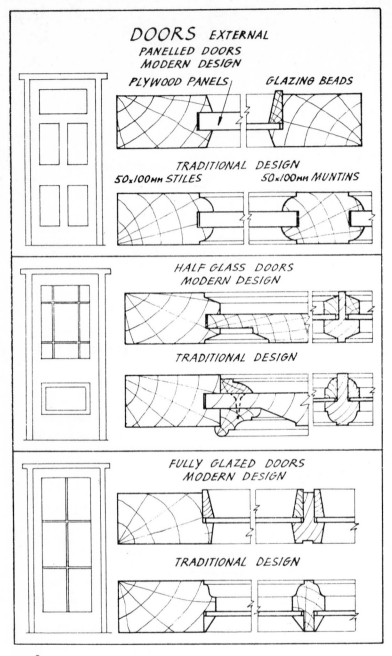

DOORS EXTERNAL

PANELLED DOORS
MODERN DESIGN

PLYWOOD PANELS   GLAZING BEADS

TRADITIONAL DESIGN
50x100mm STILES   50x100mm MUNTINS

HALF GLASS DOORS
MODERN DESIGN

TRADITIONAL DESIGN

FULLY GLAZED DOORS
MODERN DESIGN

TRADITIONAL DESIGN

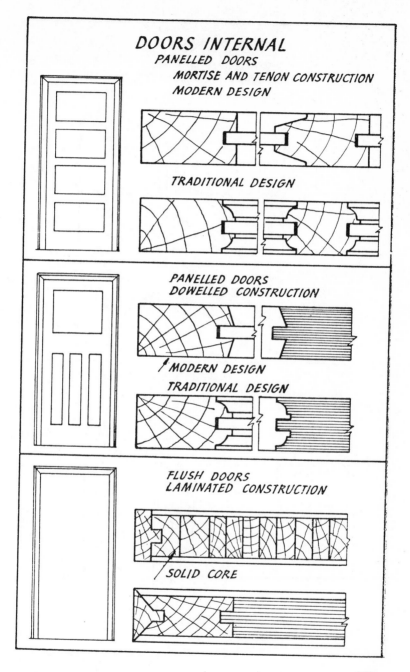

DOORS INTERNAL
PANELLED DOORS
MORTISE AND TENON CONSTRUCTION
MODERN DESIGN

TRADITIONAL DESIGN

PANELLED DOORS
DOWELLED CONSTRUCTION

MODERN DESIGN

TRADITIONAL DESIGN

FLUSH DOORS
LAMINATED CONSTRUCTION

SOLID CORE

DOORS
METHODS OF JOINTING
MORTISE. TENON AND WEDGED CONSTRUCTION

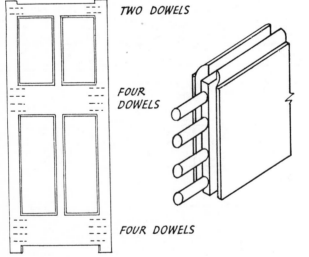

DOWELLED CONSTRUCTION

TWO DOWELS

FOUR
DOWELS

FOUR DOWELS

DOORS
METHODS OF JOINTING
LAMINATED CONSTRUCTION

SOLID CORE CONSTRUCTION

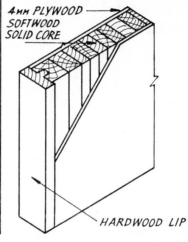

4mm PLYWOOD
SOFTWOOD
SOLID CORE

HARDWOOD LIP

FRAMED HOLLOW CORE CONSTRUCTION

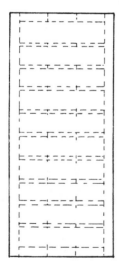

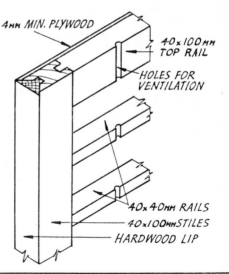

4mm MIN. PLYWOOD

40 x 100mm
TOP RAIL

HOLES FOR
VENTILATION

40 x 40mm RAILS

40 x 100mm STILES

HARDWOOD LIP

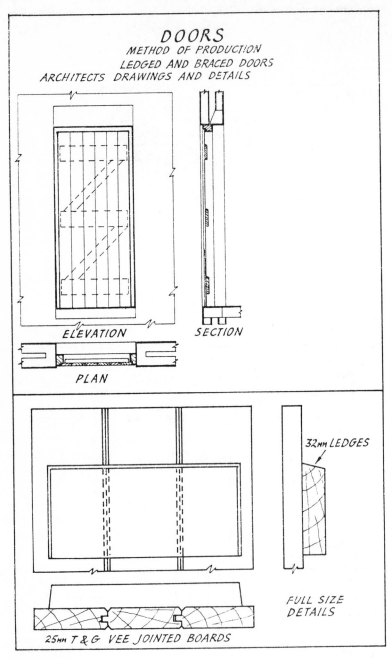

DOORS
METHOD OF PRODUCTION
LEDGED AND BRACED DOORS
ARCHITECTS DRAWINGS AND DETAILS

ELEVATION

SECTION

PLAN

32mm LEDGES

FULL SIZE
DETAILS

25mm T & G VEE JOINTED BOARDS

DOORS
METHOD OF PRODUCTION
LEDGED AND BRACED
HEIGHT AND WIDTH ROD

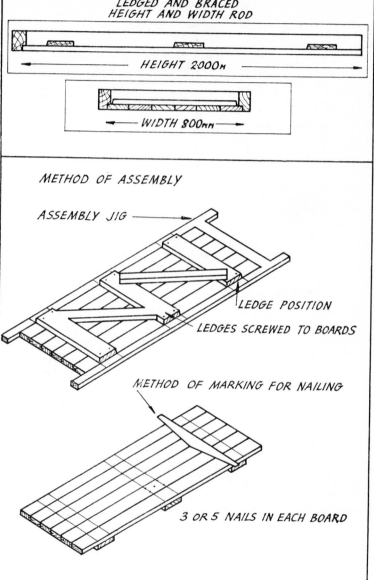

HEIGHT 2·000m

WIDTH 800mm

METHOD OF ASSEMBLY

ASSEMBLY JIG

LEDGE POSITION

LEDGES SCREWED TO BOARDS

METHOD OF MARKING FOR NAILING

3 OR 5 NAILS IN EACH BOARD

DOORS
METHOD OF PRODUCTION
TEN FOUR PANELLED DOORS
ARCHITECTS DRAWINGS & DETAILS

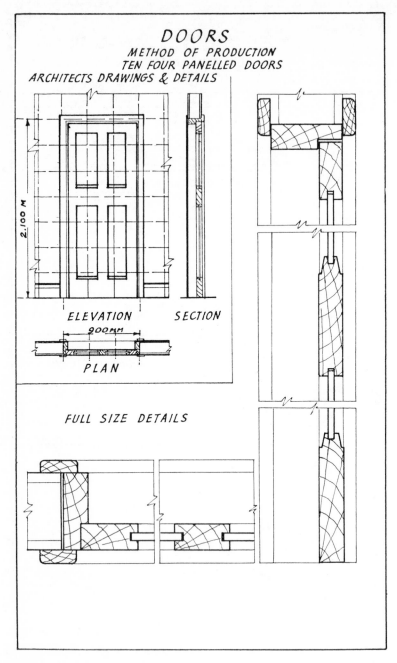

ELEVATION   SECTION

PLAN

FULL SIZE DETAILS

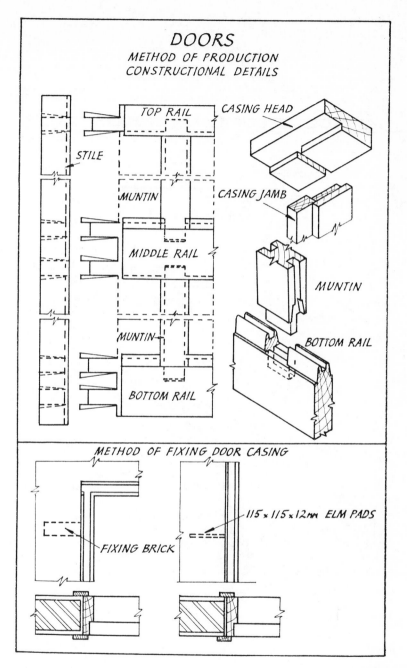

DOORS
METHOD OF PRODUCTION
CONSTRUCTIONAL DETAILS

TOP RAIL

CASING HEAD

STILE

MUNTIN

CASING JAMB

MIDDLE RAIL

MUNTIN

MUNTIN

BOTTOM RAIL

BOTTOM RAIL

METHOD OF FIXING DOOR CASING

115 x 115 x 12 mm ELM PADS

FIXING BRICK

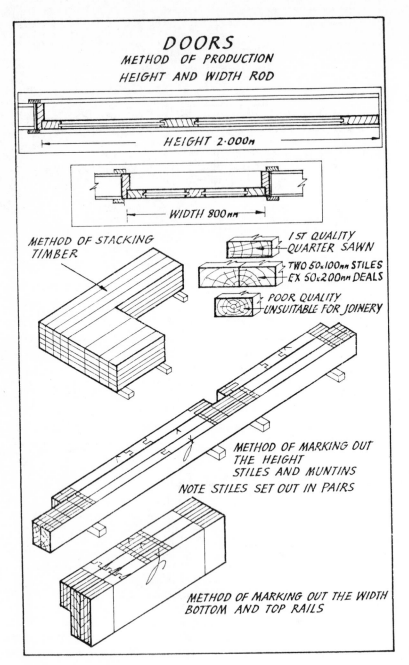

DOORS
METHOD OF PRODUCTION
HEIGHT AND WIDTH ROD

HEIGHT 2·000m

WIDTH 800mm

METHOD OF STACKING TIMBER

1ST QUALITY QUARTER SAWN

TWO 50×100mm STILES EX 50×200mm DEALS

POOR QUALITY UNSUITABLE FOR JOINERY

METHOD OF MARKING OUT THE HEIGHT STILES AND MUNTINS

NOTE STILES SET OUT IN PAIRS

METHOD OF MARKING OUT THE WIDTH BOTTOM AND TOP RAILS

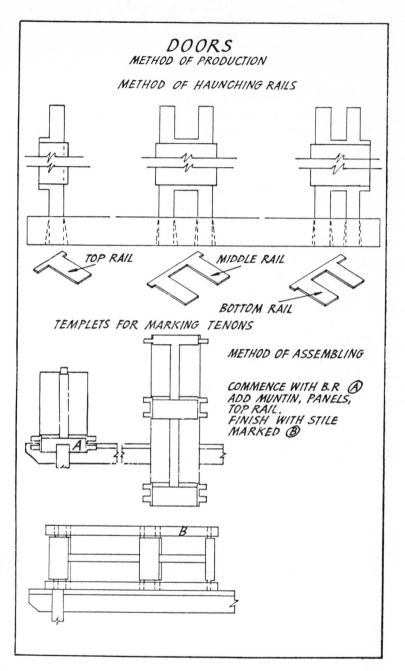

DOORS
METHOD OF PRODUCTION

METHOD OF HAUNCHING RAILS

TOP RAIL

MIDDLE RAIL

BOTTOM RAIL

TEMPLETS FOR MARKING TENONS

METHOD OF ASSEMBLING

COMMENCE WITH B.R ⓐ
ADD MUNTIN, PANELS,
TOP RAIL.
FINISH WITH STILE
MARKED ⓑ

A

B

DOORS
METHOD OF PRODUCTION

WEDGING UP

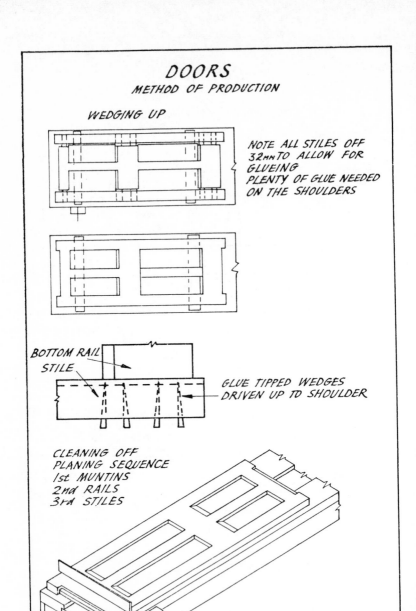

NOTE ALL STILES OFF
32mm TO ALLOW FOR
GLUEING
PLENTY OF GLUE NEEDED
ON THE SHOULDERS

BOTTOM RAIL
STILE

GLUE TIPPED WEDGES
DRIVEN UP TO SHOULDER

CLEANING OFF
PLANING SEQUENCE
1st MUNTINS
2nd RAILS
3rd STILES

The function of a window is to admit light and air to the building. The ideal window is one which is also draught- and weatherproof.

Windows in Great Britain, both traditional and modern, are of two main types—the solid window and the box or sash frame. Solid windows consist of an outer frame into which casements are fitted. Sash frames usually have a solid cill, and boxed-up jambs and head into which vertical sliding sashes are fixed. Both types are illustrated on page 146 (top).

The double hung sash window has been replaced, especially in domestic buildings, by a solid frame window of improved design.

Casement windows opening outwards and inwards are constructed with one, two, three or four lights, half of which should be made to open, as illustrated in the middle of page 146.

The name, and size details, of the various members of a casement window are given at the foot of page 146.

Standard sizes of windows

The size of wooden windows, in the past, have been governed by a combination of the casement width, usually 1 ft 8 in (508 mm), and the overall height of the window or, in the case of metal windows, the size of the casement.

During the transitional period from imperial to metric measure many windows, made to imperial sizes, will be required, and it will be an advantage to the joiner to work with a rule calibrated in metric and imperial measure.

As stated before, the BSI recommend that all components should be multiples of a 300 mm module.

The types and sizes of casement windows, in present day use,

set out on a 300 mm module, are illustrated on page 147. Full size
details of the sections are given at the foot of the page.

Design of sections

The shape of the sections plays a most important part in a window's efficiency. In order to prevent driving rain from penetrating,
grooves or throatings at least 6 mm in diameter, and usually
9 mm or more, are run or made in the rebates of the frame and the
edge of the casements (see page 148). At least 3 mm play between
casement and frame is necessary in order to take up any expansion
or movement of the frame or casement. Good and bad designs are
illustrated on page 149. Badly designed sections have small rebates
and throatings, whereas a good design has large throatings placed
near the outside.

All members of the frame are rebated to a depth of at least
12 mm to receive the casements. The horizontal members, cills and
transoms must be weathered on the top, and the weathering must
be steep enough to throw off any water.

Rules to be observed in designing window sections

1 All rebates for casements should be 12 to 15 mm deep.
2 All rebates for glass should be 9 mm deep.
3 Throatings should be not less than 6 mm in diameter.

The traditional window has not changed much in the design of
the sections and, if properly constructed from sound materials,
will still give satisfaction. Casements which open present the
greatest problem. To be draughtproof they need to be tight fitting,
and this usually means that they cannot be opened or closed
during the winter.

Much research has gone into the design and production of a
standard type of window, and the result of this is the lipped casement window. This type has many advantages over the traditional
design. It is reasonably draughtproof, needs very little maintenance, and its casements will open all the year round.

The most modern developments in window design tend towards
simplicity in jointing and glazing (see page 150). The introduction
of waterproof adhesives may account for this, since these have
eliminated the need for wedging and pinning. Glazing fillets and

the use of fillets to form the rebates have also eliminated the necessity for rebating and moulding.

Draughtproof construction

The sash window form of construction, as used in the traditional window, is the best for keeping out draughts. The outside linings and parting beads cover the sashes.

The first real step forward in solid window design, as has been said, was the introduction of the lipped casement. This provides cover for the joint between the casement and frame. The play between casement and frame could therefore be increased from 2 to 4 mm, eliminating any need for easing after the casement has been fitted.

Windows which are adequately draughtproof are very difficult to make when one is using materials such as timber or metal, but a very high percentage of efficiency can be obtained by the introduction of softer material in the form of tape. This has been done for many years on the Continent, usually on double glazed, pivot-hung, single pane windows. The tape is usually inserted into the corner of the rebates of the frame, on to which the opening casements fit snugly when closed.

Constructional details

It is interesting to notice that in the construction of windows, and indeed in many other types of joinery work, two distinct methods of framing are used—one for the fixed parts and another for the moving parts. The fixed parts constitute the frame, and the moving parts the casements. In the frame the outside horizontal members, heads and cills, are mortised; and the vertical members, jambs and mullions, are tenoned into them. In the casements the vertical members, stiles, are mortised, and the horizontal members, rails and bars, are tenoned into these.

Operations involved in making windows

Architect's drawings and details

In order to make a window the joiner requires drawings which give him its size and the shape of each member, a specification of the materials and method of construction, and, on large building work, a bill of quantities giving the amount of material and labour to be employed.

The windows are shown on the main drawings of the building, which are drawn to a scale of 1:100 or 1:50. Each size of window appears on a larger scale, together with details of its exact position in the wall. In this drawing the scale is 1:20, and for this reason the drawings are called layout details.

The most important details for the joiner are the full size ones which give the shape and section size of each member. The 1:20 and full size details are illustrated on page 151.

Sequence of operations

The importance of working methodically when producing a piece of craft work cannot be too strongly emphasised. Each operation must be carried out accurately, and in the right sequence, if one is to get a high standard of finish. Here is an example to illustrate these points. Twenty windows, each with one light, are to be made. They are 450 mm wide and 675 mm high, and are shown on page 151.

The order in which these operations are performed is the same, with one or two exceptions, whether they are being done by hand or by machine. The following sequence would apply to most framed-up joinery work:

1   Prepare the height and width rods. These are shown set out on page 152 (foot). The rods may be of paper, or thin softwood board, preferably 175 to 275 mm wide. The boards are easier to read if they are white, so they are generally rubbed with chalk.

2   Prepare the cutting list (see page 143).

3   Cut out the material to size. For good quality work the sections should be cut from bigger timbers. For example, 75×100 mm framing is cut from 75×200 mm or 75×225 mm deals, and 50×50 mm casement stiles from 50×225 mm deals.

4   Plane up the material to size. Whether this is done by hand or by machine, it is essential that the wood should be kept properly stacked so that it will not twist or warp.

5   Mark out the material. This must be done accurately. Every line drawn on the timber should have a purpose. Unnecessary lines

Job No.   20 1 light windows   450 mm wide
                                                                     675 mm high

Member	No.	Cutting size (mm)	Finished size (mm)	Material
Frame				
Cills	20	600 × 75 × 150	72 × 147	English Oak
Heads	20	600 × 75 × 100	72 × 97	European redwood
Jambs	40	700 × 75 × 100	72 × 97	,,
Casements Stiles	40	670 × 45 × 50	42 × 47	,,
Top rail	20	410 × 45 × 50	42 × 47	,,
Bott. rail	20	410 × 45 × 75	42 × 72	,,

only make for confusion, and are very often the cause of mistakes. The diagrams on page 153 show how each member should be marked out. Begin on the edge of each, marking the overall sizes first.

NOTE   Use the actual member for marking out its size.

For accurate work it is best to use a marking knife for marking out on the face edges and shoulder lines, and a pencil for marking the wedge room on the back edge; but a good, hard, firm pencil can quite well be used for both.

6   Mortise and rip tenons only (if done by hand). All the mortising should be carried out in one operation, starting, say, with twenty heads, passing on to twenty cills, and ending with forty stiles. Tenon ripping should be done in the same way.

7   Do all rebating, grooving, moulding, and work any plaster keys that may be necessary. Only the plaster key and rebating are needed in this case. If the rebates are large ones, much of the waste is removed by ploughing.

8   Perform shoulder cutting and haunching. This should be done in one operation, dealing first with twenty pairs of jambs, then

with twenty top rails, and then with twenty bottom rails. Finally, the forty rails should be haunched.

9 Clean up all edges and parts that are inaccessible when the framing has been assembled. This should be done with considerable care. It is usual to clean up all the frame members' surfaces, leaving only the joints to be cleaned off when the frame is assembled.

10 Mitre and scribe if necessary. In this case it is not.

11 Wedge up. The diagrams on page 154 show the operations involved. It is usual to leave the joints about 25 mm off so that the glue can be spread on the shoulders. It is common practice to wedge and pin the frames, using a 9 mm dowel for the pins. The wedges should be driven right up to the shoulder, and great care should be taken when one is testing for square.

12 Clean off all surfaces. The casements need cleaning off on each side, and care should be taken to keep them flat on the face. Generally, the faces of the frames should be cleaned off as each frame is put together.

13 Fit and hang the casements. Cut off the horns, fit the casement into the frame, fit the hinges, and hang it.

Practice lessons

1 Working from the information given:

    (a) Draw the elevation views of three types of solid casement windows, as illustrated on page 147.

    (b) Draw, full size, the sectional details, as illustrated at the foot of the page.

2 *(a)* Make neat diagrams to show the construction of solid window frames and casements. See page 152.

    (b) Draw full size section details to illustrate good and bad window design. Show clearly the proportions of rebates, throatings, and lipped casements.

3 Working from the instructions given:

    (a) Set out a workshop rod for the one light window illustrated on page 151.

    (b) Carry out all the operations involved in making the frame and casement up to the wedging up stage.

    (c) Assemble, wedge up, and clean off the frame and casement.

    (d) Fit and hang the casement.

    (e) Fit and fix the casement stay and fastener.

WINDOWS

SOLID CASEMENT WINDOW

SASH WINDOW

DOUBLE GLAZED PIVOT HUNG WINDOW

SOLID CASEMENT WINDOWS

NOTE   DIAGONAL LINES INDICATE OPENING CASEMENTS

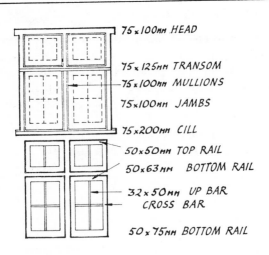

75 x 100mm HEAD

75 x 125mm TRANSOM

75 x 100mm MULLIONS

75 x 100mm JAMBS

75 x 200mm CILL

50 x 50mm TOP RAIL

50 x 63mm BOTTOM RAIL

32 x 50mm UP BAR
CROSS BAR

50 x 75mm BOTTOM RAIL

WINDOWS

SOLID CASEMENT WINDOWS

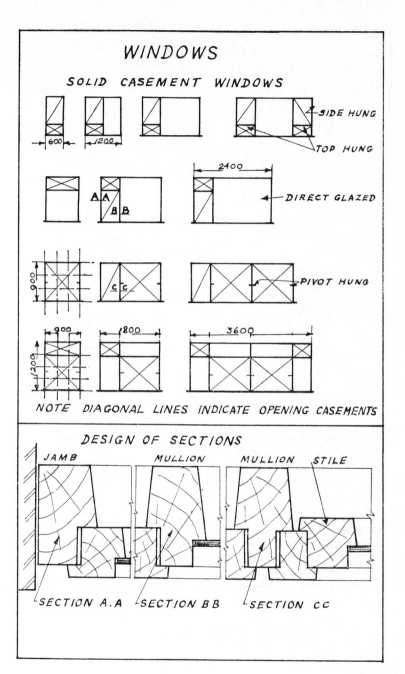

SIDE HUNG

TOP HUNG

DIRECT GLAZED

PIVOT HUNG

NOTE DIAGONAL LINES INDICATE OPENING CASEMENTS

DESIGN OF SECTIONS

JAMB   MULLION   MULLION   STILE

SECTION A.A   SECTION BB   SECTION CC

147

WINDOWS
DESIGN OF SECTIONS IN PRESENT DAY USE

TRADITIONAL CONSTRUCTION

WEATHER PROOF CONSTRUCTION

HEADS

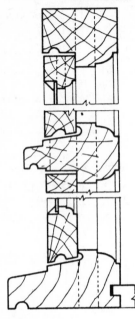

TOP RAILS

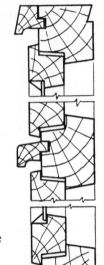

BOTTOM RAILS

TRANSOMS

TOP RAILS

BOTTOM RAILS

CILLS

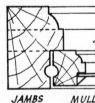

JAMBS   MULLIONS   STILES

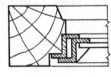

JAMBS

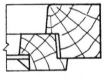

METAL CASEMENTS IN WOOD SURROUNDS

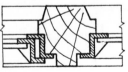

148

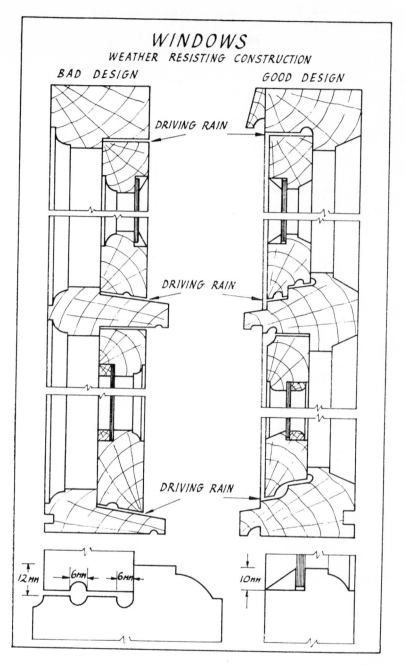

WINDOWS
WEATHER RESISTING CONSTRUCTION

BAD DESIGN

GOOD DESIGN

DRIVING RAIN

DRIVING RAIN

DRIVING RAIN

12mm 6mm 6mm

10mm

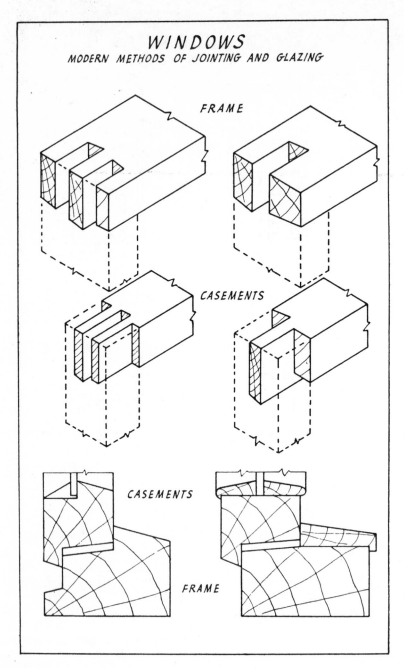

WINDOWS
MODERN METHODS OF JOINTING AND GLAZING

FRAME

CASEMENTS

CASEMENTS

FRAME

WORKSHOP PRACTICE
OPERATIONS INVOLVED IN MAKING WINDOWS

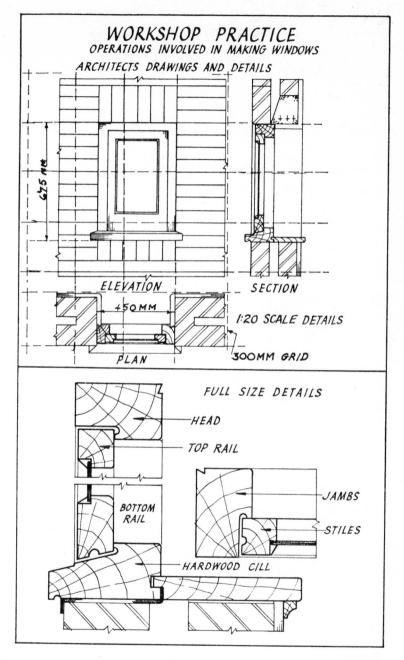

ARCHITECTS DRAWINGS AND DETAILS

675 MM

ELEVATION

SECTION

450MM

1:20 SCALE DETAILS

PLAN

300MM GRID

FULL SIZE DETAILS

HEAD

TOP RAIL

JAMBS

BOTTOM RAIL

STILES

HARDWOOD CILL

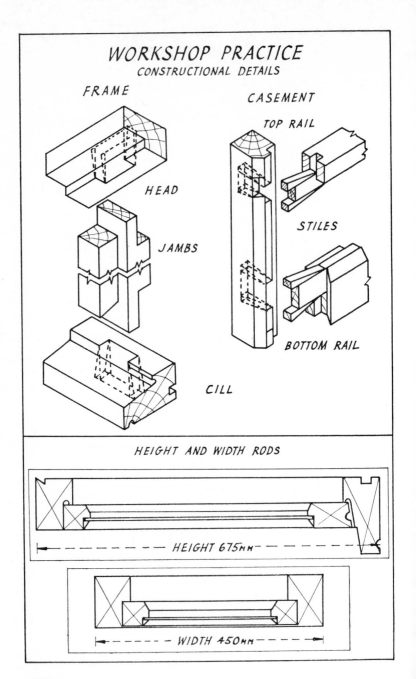

WORKSHOP PRACTICE
CONSTRUCTIONAL DETAILS

FRAME

CASEMENT

TOP RAIL

HEAD

STILES

JAMBS

BOTTOM RAIL

CILL

HEIGHT AND WIDTH RODS

HEIGHT 675ᴍᴍ

WIDTH 450ᴍᴍ

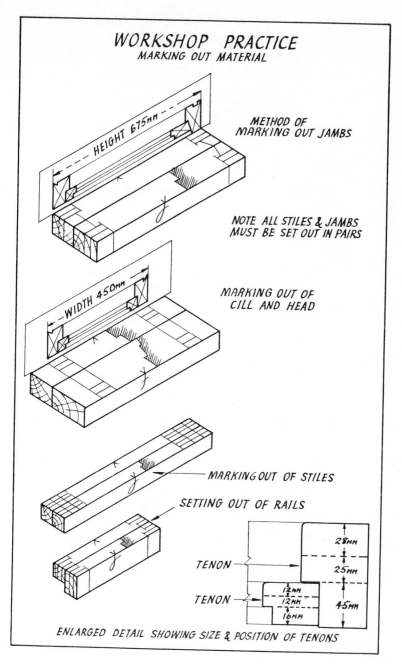

WORKSHOP PRACTICE
MARKING OUT MATERIAL

HEIGHT 675mm

METHOD OF
MARKING OUT JAMBS

NOTE ALL STILES & JAMBS
MUST BE SET OUT IN PAIRS

WIDTH 450mm

MARKING OUT OF
CILL AND HEAD

MARKING OUT OF STILES

SETTING OUT OF RAILS

TENON

TENON

28mm

25mm

12mm

12mm

45mm

16mm

ENLARGED DETAIL SHOWING SIZE & POSITION OF TENONS

WORKSHOP PRACTICE
WEDGING UP, GLUEING UP AND CLEANING OFF OF FRAME AND CASEMENTS

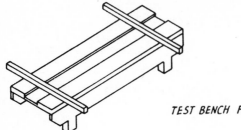

TEST BENCH FOR WINDING

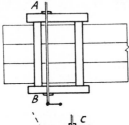

FRAME

① CRAMP UP AND FASTEN JOINTS A & B

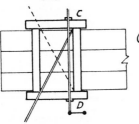

② MOVE CRAMP TO JOINTS C & D TEST FOR SQUARE WITH SQUARING ROD AND FASTEN

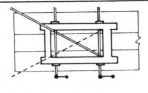

CASEMENTS

① FIX CRAMPS ON BENCH
GLUE JOINTS
CLAMP UP, TEST FOR SQUARE
DRIVE IN WEDGES
STACK FOR DRYING

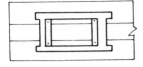

② CLEAN OFF BOTH SIDES

154

The traditional timber partition consists of vertical studs, jointed on to a head and cill at each end.

A *framed* (trussed) partition is of heavy construction and is made in the same way as a roof truss, with a cill, a head and struts forming a complete trussed frame. This used to provide some support for the floor above. The framed type of partition is rarely used today, since the need for it has been eliminated by better forms of construction.

Details of a common timber partition are given on page 157 (top), where the size and spacing of the members, and the treatment of the door openings are shown.

Page 157 (foot) shows three methods of constructing *soundproof partitions*, together with enlarged details of the arrangement of the studs and insulating materials. The isometric drawings on page 158 show more clearly the three distinct methods of construction.

There are many insulating materials which can be used for making partitions. They can be got in slab, board or roll form, and include slag wool, fibre glass, fibre boards, chip boards, straw boards, and felts.

Operations involved in building partitions

Much of this work is prefabricated, and is delivered ready to assemble and erect. The various methods of construction are illustrated on page 159.

Partitions may be trenched, or mortised and tenoned together. It is usual to mortise and tenon if the work is prefabricated, but when the work is assembled on the job the trenching method is used.

NOTE The nogging pieces are cut in between the studs and are not trenched or tenoned.

Practice lessons

1   Working from the information given:

    (a) Draw the elevation view of a common or stud partition, as illustrated on page 157. Scale 1:20.

    (b) Prepare full size details of the door opening.

2   *(a)* Draw, to a suitable scale, isometric constructional details of a stud partition.

    (b) Make neat diagrams to show the construction of a soundproof partition.

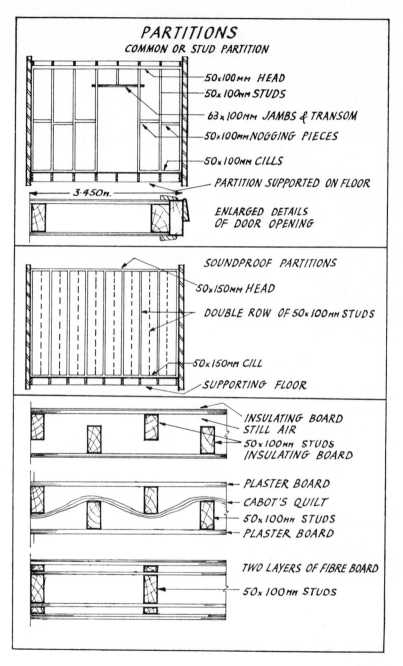

PARTITIONS
COMMON OR STUD PARTITION

50x100mm HEAD

50x100mm STUDS

63x100mm JAMBS & TRANSOM

50x100mm NOGGING PIECES

50x100mm CILLS

PARTITION SUPPORTED ON FLOOR

3·450m.

ENLARGED DETAILS
OF DOOR OPENING

SOUNDPROOF PARTITIONS

50x150mm HEAD

DOUBLE ROW OF 50x100mm STUDS

50x150mm CILL

SUPPORTING FLOOR

INSULATING BOARD
STILL AIR
50x100mm STUDS
INSULATING BOARD

PLASTER BOARD
CABOT'S QUILT
50x100mm STUDS
PLASTER BOARD

TWO LAYERS OF FIBRE BOARD

50x100mm STUDS

PARTITIONS
DETAILS OF METHODS OF CONSTRUCTION

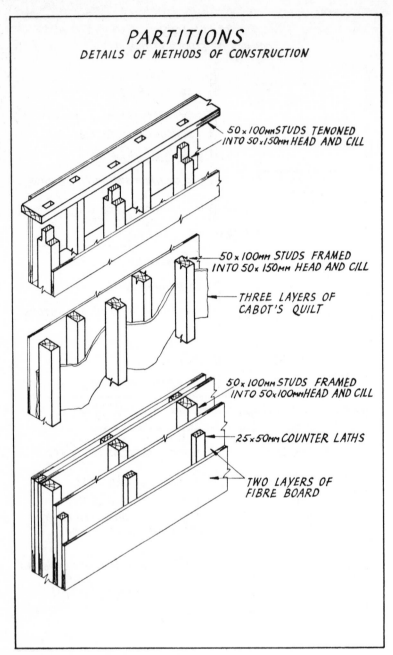

50 x 100mm STUDS TENONED INTO 50 x 150mm HEAD AND CILL

50 x 100mm STUDS FRAMED INTO 50 x 150mm HEAD AND CILL

THREE LAYERS OF CABOT'S QUILT

50 x 100mm STUDS FRAMED INTO 50 x 100mm HEAD AND CILL

25 x 50mm COUNTER LATHS

TWO LAYERS OF FIBRE BOARD

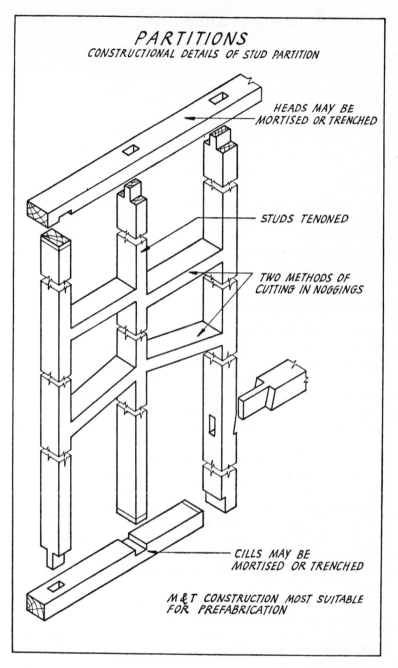

PARTITIONS
CONSTRUCTIONAL DETAILS OF STUD PARTITION

HEADS MAY BE
MORTISED OR TRENCHED

STUDS TENONED

TWO METHODS OF
CUTTING IN NOGGINGS

CILLS MAY BE
MORTISED OR TRENCHED

M & T CONSTRUCTION MOST SUITABLE
FOR PREFABRICATION

13 | Finishings and fixings

Door openings and many window openings are finished with casings or linings. The width of these casings varies with the thickness of the wall; 115 mm walls would have 150 mm casings, 225 mm walls 280 mm casings, and 350 mm walls 375 mm casings (see page 164).

Casings and finishings

Architraves provide a finish for the openings, and vary in size from 12 × 40 mm to 40 × 150 mm. When larger architraves are required, they are usually built up in two or more pieces.

Skirtings act as a finish between the floor and walls. They vary in size from 18 × 50 mm to 32 × 225 mm. Like architraves, larger sections are built up in two or more pieces.

Picture and dado rails vary in size from 18 × 40 mm to 32 × 100 mm.

Door casings, each of which consists of a pair of jambs and a head, are made 32 to 40 mm thick. They may be tongued and grooved together or else dovetailed; in Britain it is common practice to tongue and groove. The jambs are tongued into the head, and the joint secured with nails or screws. With hardwood joinery it is usual to assemble the casings in the shop, but in general joinery they are commonly assembled on the job.

Page 165 (top) gives details of 150 mm casings of traditional design.

Page 165 (foot) gives details of 280 mm casings, showing solid and built-up construction with wrot grounds.

Enlarged details of skirtings, dado rails, picture rails, and architraves are shown on page 166.

Fixing

There are two stages involved in fixing joinery work into a building. In the first stage all the grounds, including wrot grounds, profiles, linings and door casings, are fixed. Then skirtings, architraves, doors (fitting and hanging) and any other necessary fixing should be completed before one begins on the final stage of painting and decorating.

Details of the method of assembling and fixing door casings are given on page 167 (top). The casings are fixed to elm pads or fixing bricks as shown at the foot of the page.

NOTE No difficulties will arise when hanging the doors if the floors are level and the casings plumb.

Linings require a certain amount of preparation before they are fixed. This preparation and fixing is illustrated on page 168.

Skirtings may be fixed to plugs, grounds or fixing bricks. Page 169 (top) gives the plan of a room to be fitted with skirtings. The way to plug is shown below. Lengths of skirting, 12 to 25 mm longer than each wall length, should be cut into place and scribed, if necessary, to the floor. The internal angles have scribed joints, and the external ones are mitred.

The method of forming the joints and fixing the skirting is shown in detail on page 170.

The fixing of *picture and dado rails* involves operations similar to those used when one is dealing with skirting.

NOTE Care must be taken to keep each length straight and level.

Each set of *architraves* consists of one pair of jambs and one head. It is best to start by fixing a jamb, then dealing with the head and finally with the other jamb. This avoids the need to joint a member at both ends.

Nails should be placed in the quirks, evenly spaced, and punched in.

NOTE All finishing members in good class work should be cleaned up to the same standard as the framed joinery.

It is essential that the fixing joiner should have the right equipment. He needs, in addition to a saw bench, a small work bench, cramps, a plumb rule and level.

Practice lessons

1   Working from the information given:

 (a)   Draw, full size, the sectional view of three types of skirting.

 (b)   Make neat diagrams to show how the skirtings are fixed to the walls.

 (c)   Make neat diagrams to show how the skirtings are jointed at the internal, and external, angles.

2   *(a)*   Draw to a 1:5 scale the section of a 32 × 150 mm casing as illustrated on page 165.

 (b)   Make neat diagrams to show how the casing is fixed into the prepared opening.

3   Draw full size sections of:

 (a)   A 25 × 75 mm dado rail

 (b)   A 25 × 50 mm picture rail

 (c)   A 40 × 150 mm built up architrave.

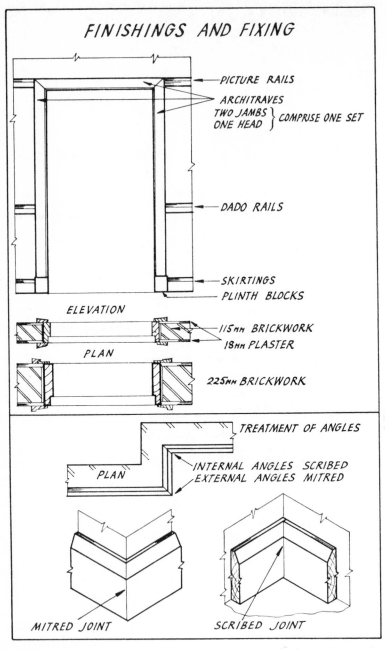

FINISHINGS AND FIXING

PICTURE RAILS

ARCHITRAVES

TWO JAMBS
ONE HEAD } COMPRISE ONE SET

DADO RAILS

SKIRTINGS
PLINTH BLOCKS

ELEVATION

115mm BRICKWORK

18mm PLASTER

PLAN

225mm BRICKWORK

TREATMENT OF ANGLES

PLAN

INTERNAL ANGLES SCRIBED
EXTERNAL ANGLES MITRED

MITRED JOINT

SCRIBED JOINT

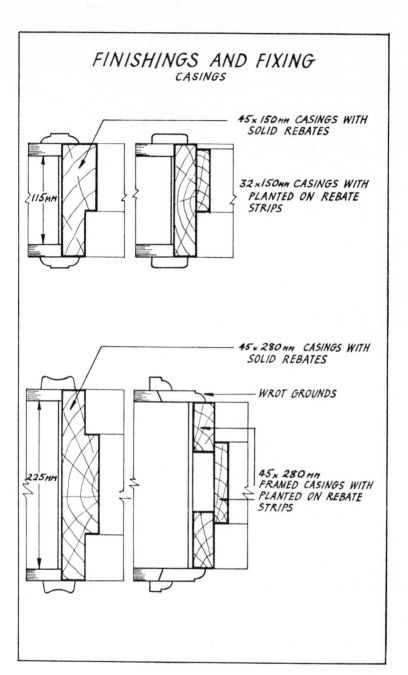

FINISHINGS AND FIXING
CASINGS

45 x 150mm CASINGS WITH SOLID REBATES

32 x 150mm CASINGS WITH PLANTED ON REBATE STRIPS

115mm

45 x 280mm CASINGS WITH SOLID REBATES

WROT GROUNDS

225mm

45 x 280mm FRAMED CASINGS WITH PLANTED ON REBATE STRIPS

FINISHINGS AND FIXING

BOARD SKIRTINGS

DETAILS OF TYPICAL
SKIRTINGS
DADO & PICTURE RAILS
ARCHITRAVES

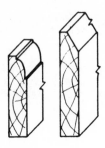
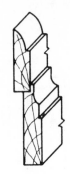

COVE SKIRTINGS

DADO RAILS

PICTURE RAILS

SOLID ARCHITRAVES

BUILT UP ARCHITRAVES

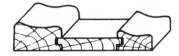

166

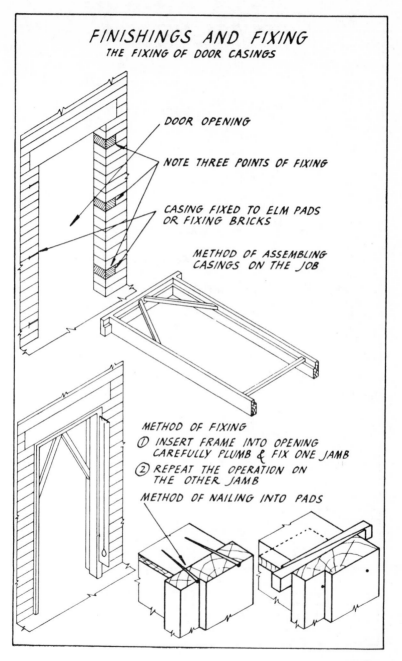

FINISHINGS AND FIXING
THE FIXING OF DOOR CASINGS

DOOR OPENING

NOTE THREE POINTS OF FIXING

CASING FIXED TO ELM PADS
OR FIXING BRICKS

METHOD OF ASSEMBLING
CASINGS ON THE JOB

METHOD OF FIXING
① INSERT FRAME INTO OPENING
CAREFULLY PLUMB & FIX ONE JAMB
② REPEAT THE OPERATION ON
THE OTHER JAMB

METHOD OF NAILING INTO PADS

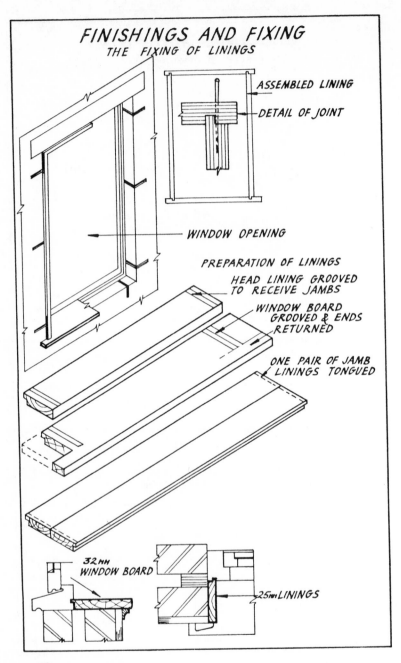

FINISHINGS AND FIXING
THE FIXING OF LININGS

ASSEMBLED LINING

DETAIL OF JOINT

WINDOW OPENING

PREPARATION OF LININGS

HEAD LINING GROOVED
TO RECEIVE JAMBS

WINDOW BOARD
GROOVED & ENDS
RETURNED

ONE PAIR OF JAMB
LININGS TONGUED

32 мм
WINDOW BOARD

25мм LININGS

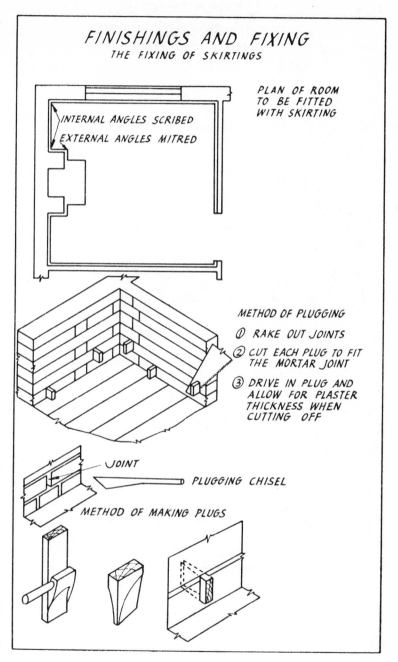

FINISHINGS AND FIXING
THE FIXING OF SKIRTINGS

PLAN OF ROOM
TO BE FITTED
WITH SKIRTING

INTERNAL ANGLES SCRIBED

EXTERNAL ANGLES MITRED

METHOD OF PLUGGING

① RAKE OUT JOINTS

② CUT EACH PLUG TO FIT
THE MORTAR JOINT

③ DRIVE IN PLUG AND
ALLOW FOR PLASTER
THICKNESS WHEN
CUTTING OFF

JOINT

PLUGGING CHISEL

METHOD OF MAKING PLUGS

169

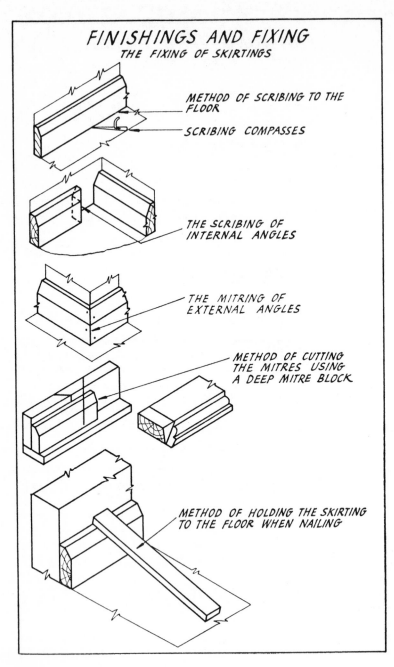

FINISHINGS AND FIXING
THE FIXING OF SKIRTINGS

METHOD OF SCRIBING TO THE FLOOR

SCRIBING COMPASSES

THE SCRIBING OF INTERNAL ANGLES

THE MITRING OF EXTERNAL ANGLES

METHOD OF CUTTING THE MITRES USING A DEEP MITRE BLOCK

METHOD OF HOLDING THE SKIRTING TO THE FLOOR WHEN NAILING

The main function of a stairway is to give access to floors of varying levels. They may be classified according to their shape in plan, or to the method of constructing the strings.

Classification according to plan

Timber stairs can roughly be divided into two classes—newel and non-newel. The non-newel types include stairs between walls, and stairs with continued strings and handrails. The newel type includes open straight flights, dog-leg stairs, and open newel stairs.

NOTE The newel post is the essential part of the construction.

Straight flights are built up from a series of steps called fliers. Each step is formed by a tread and riser, supported by strings in which they are housed and wedged. Two illustrations are shown on page 175, one of a flight between walls, and the other of a newel type of staircase. The newels give support to each end of the open strings.

The *dog-leg stair* is so named because it resembles the hind legs of a dog in the vertical section view. It consists of two straight flights connected by a half space landing. Only one newel is provided on the landing, into which the lower and upper strings are tenoned. This arrangement presents difficulties in the finishing of the handrail and balusters.

Classification according to construction of strings

Three methods of constructing strings are shown on page 176 (top):

1   Close or housed strings with cappings to receive balusters
2   Cut strings finished with return steps and brackets
3   Continuous strings and handrails.

The detailed construction of the strings, treads, risers and newels is given on page 176 (foot).

The planning of stairs

The following four important rules concern the joiner:

(a)   Sufficient headroom must be provided. The diagram on page 177 (top) gives the minimum headroom (2·000 m) measured vertically from the face of the riser and tread.

(b)   The width of the stairs will vary according to the class of building. Public buildings need stairs 1·400 to 2·000 m wide, but domestic buildings can have stairs only 0·850 to 1·000 m in width (see page 177—second drawing).

(c)   Handrails should be fixed at a height where they can be comfortably held, but which is yet high enough to prevent accidents. The height over the steps, measured vertically from the face of riser and tread to the top of the handrail, should be 0·760 to 0·860 m, and the height on the landings should be 0·950 to 1·150 m (see page 177—third drawing).

(d)   To produce a stair that is not tiring or awkward to ascend or descend, the going should bear a certain ratio to the rise. It can be assumed that the average length of step in walking is 600 mm, and it is twice as tiring to climb upward as it is to walk forward. The best methods of obtaining the rise and going are as follows (page 177—foot):

1   One going plus two risers should equal 60 to 62 cm.

Example   going 25 cm + twice rise = 61 cm

$$\text{twice rise} = 61 - 25 = 36$$

$$\text{rise} = \frac{36}{2} = 18 \text{ cm or } 180 \text{ mm}$$

2   Rise multiplied by going should equal 450.

Example   going 25 cm × rise = 450

$$\text{rise} = \frac{450}{25} = 18 \text{ cm or } 180 \text{ mm}$$

Operations involved in building a straight flight of stairs

The architect's drawings and details are given on page 178.
  The specification reads:
40 × 250 mm wall strings
32 mm treads
25 mm risers
50 × 75 mm handrail.

Sequence of operations

1   Take the measurements from the job in hand, of the total rise
from floor to floor and the width.
2   Calculate the rise and going per step.
3   Prepare a cutting list.
4   Make a pitchboard and tread and riser sticks.
5   Using these and a margin templet, mark out the strings, treads
and risers. This operation is shown on page 179 (top).

NOTE   It is assumed that all timber is planed.

6   Work all the members, trenching the strings and tonguing and
grooving the treads and risers. Page 179 (middle) shows the wall
strings marked out in pairs, the templet for the treads and risers,
and a way of trenching the strings by hand.
7   Clean up all visible surfaces.
8   Work the casings at the upper and lower ends of the strings.
9   Assemble the stairs, and glue and wedge the steps into the
strings. In good class hardwood stairs, each tread and riser is glued
together, and the ends of each step are fitted into the trenched
strings as shown on page 180. Page 180 (foot) shows how to
assemble the stairs when using a special bench.

NOTE   Many straight flights between walls must be assembled
when in position.

Practice lessons

1 Working from the information given:

   (a) Draw the plan and elevation view of the straight flight of stairs as illustrated on page 178. Scale 1:20.

   (b) Prepare 1:5 scale details showing the steps, trimmer and handrail.

2 Working from the information given on page 179, make neat diagrams to show:

   (a) Minimum headroom.
   (b) Minimum width of stairs.
   (c) Height of handrails.
   (d) Proportion of rise and going.

3 Make neat sketches to explain the following stair-building terms.

   (a) Storey rod.
   (b) Pitchboard.
   (c) Tread and riser sticks.

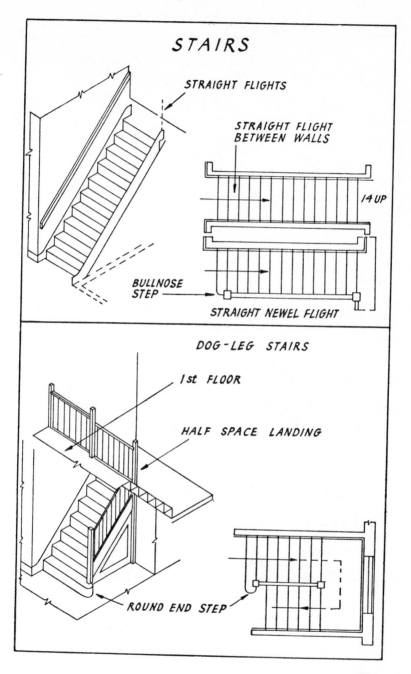

STAIRS

STRAIGHT FLIGHTS

STRAIGHT FLIGHT
BETWEEN WALLS

14 UP

BULLNOSE
STEP

STRAIGHT NEWEL FLIGHT

DOG-LEG STAIRS

1st FLOOR

HALF SPACE LANDING

ROUND END STEP

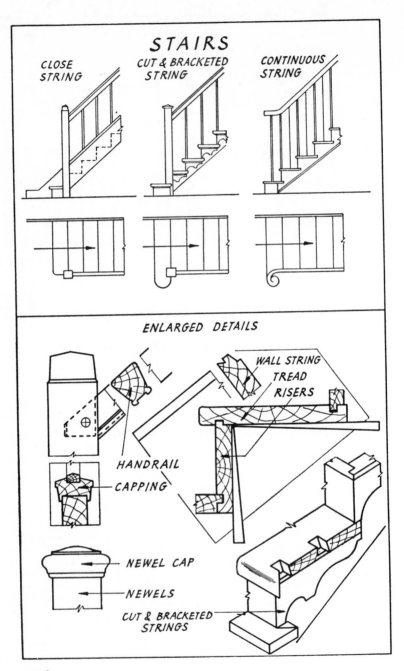

STAIRS

CLOSE STRING

CUT & BRACKETED STRING

CONTINUOUS STRING

ENLARGED DETAILS

WALL STRING
TREAD
RISERS

HANDRAIL

CAPPING

NEWEL CAP

NEWELS

CUT & BRACKETED STRINGS

STAIRS
PLANNING HEADROOM

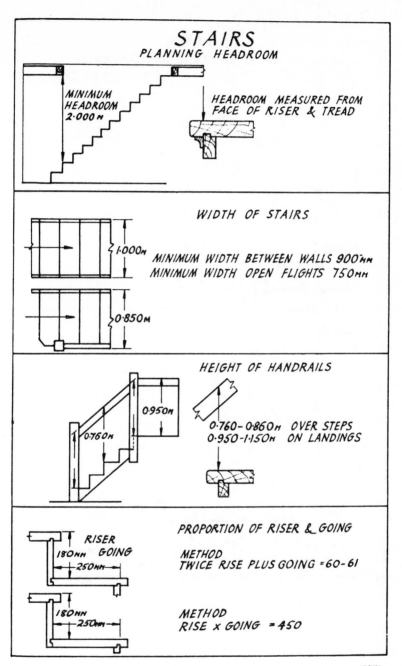

MINIMUM HEADROOM 2·000 M

HEADROOM MEASURED FROM FACE OF RISER & TREAD

WIDTH OF STAIRS

1·000 M

MINIMUM WIDTH BETWEEN WALLS 900 MM
MINIMUM WIDTH OPEN FLIGHTS 750 MM

0·850 M

HEIGHT OF HANDRAILS

0·950 M

0·760 M

0·760 – 0·860 M OVER STEPS
0·950 – 1·150 M ON LANDINGS

PROPORTION OF RISER & GOING

RISER
GOING
180 MM
250 MM

METHOD
TWICE RISE PLUS GOING = 60 – 61

180 MM
250 MM

METHOD
RISE × GOING = 450

STAIRS
STRAIGHT FLIGHT OF STAIRS BETWEEN WALLS
ARCHITECTS DRAWINGS

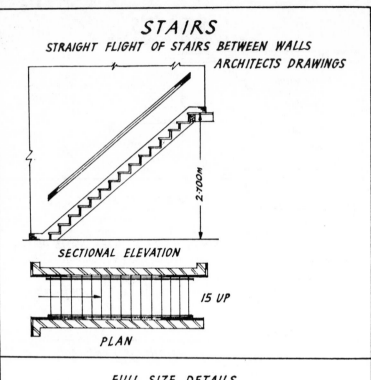

2·700M

SECTIONAL ELEVATION

15 UP

PLAN

FULL SIZE DETAILS

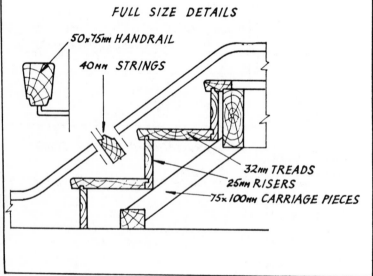

50x75mm HANDRAIL

40mm STRINGS

32mm TREADS
25mm RISERS
75x100mm CARRIAGE PIECES

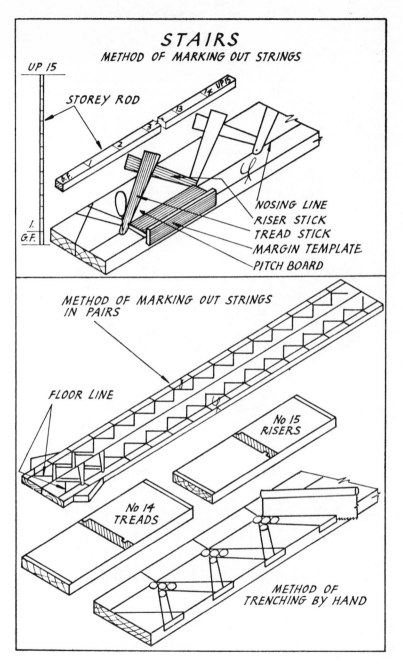

STAIRS
METHOD OF MARKING OUT STRINGS

UP 15

STOREY ROD

UP 15
3
3
2
G.F.

1.
G.F.

NOSING LINE
RISER STICK
TREAD STICK
MARGIN TEMPLATE
PITCH BOARD

METHOD OF MARKING OUT STRINGS
IN PAIRS

FLOOR LINE

No 15
RISERS

No 14
TREADS

METHOD OF
TRENCHING BY HAND

179

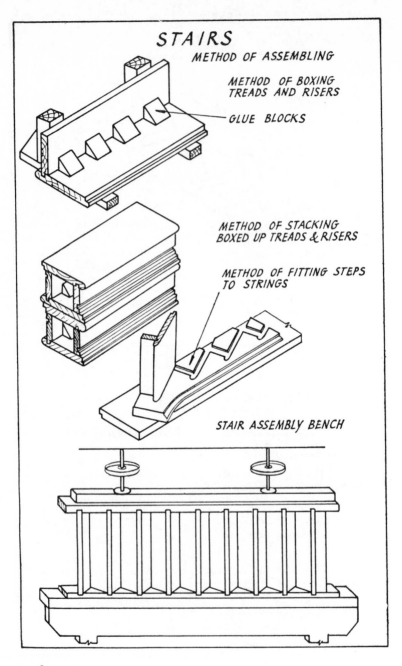

STAIRS

METHOD OF ASSEMBLING

METHOD OF BOXING
TREADS AND RISERS

GLUE BLOCKS

METHOD OF STACKING
BOXED UP TREADS & RISERS

METHOD OF FITTING STEPS
TO STRINGS

STAIR ASSEMBLY BENCH

Timbers are divided into two main classes—softwoods and hardwoods. Softwoods (pines, firs, spruces) have needle-like leaves; their wood is resinous and, with one or two exceptions, easy to work. Hardwoods—for example, oak, ash, beech and teak—on the other hand have broad leaves; the wood is non-resinous, and is usually more difficult to work than softwood. Page 189 (top) shows a typical softwood (Scots Pine), with enlarged views of the bole and leaves (notice the seed cones). Page 189 (foot) shows a hardwood (oak) with enlarged views of the bole and leaves.

The structure of timber

The structure of a tree is of a complex, cellular character. The central core is the pith, and the irregular concentric rings of tissue forming the heart wood and sapwood are called annual rings. Each ring represents one year's growth, but its thickness will vary, since a dry season limits growth and produces a narrow ring, whereas a good year will produce a wide ring.

The ring is divided into an inner portion, called the spring wood, and an outer portion called the summer wood. The cells of the spring wood have relatively thin walls and large cavities, but the summer wood cells have thicker walls and smaller cavities.

The softwood's honeycombed structure is shown on page 190 (top). The tubular cells are called tracheids, and are arranged in rows, separated at intervals by the medullary rays.

The cells communicate with each other through holes in their sides, called pits.

The structure of a hardwood is more complicated. It consists of pores or vessels, fibres, soft tissue, and medullary rays. The vessels are placed round the open-ended cells which extend down the trunk of the tree. The vessels vary in size; some hardwoods, such as ash, elm, and oak, have relatively large vessels concentrated within the spring wood, and these woods are called ring porous. Other hardwoods, such as mahogany, beech and birch, have vessels fairly uniformly scattered over the whole growth ring, and are termed diffuse-porous.

The structure of hardwoods is shown on page 190 (foot).

Identification of timbers

Examination with a microscope is necessary to identify specimens of timber. Hardwoods are identified on their transverse and tangential sections; softwoods on their tangential and radial sections.

Conversion of timber

Large quantities of timber are imported into Great Britain. Softwoods come largely from Scandinavia, Russia and America; and hardwoods from Europe, Africa, India, America and Japan. Softwoods are converted into marketable sizes before export by the timber-producing countries. The processes involved (felling, transportation to the mills and conversion into planks, boards and scantling) are all highly mechanised. In the Scandinavian countries much of the softwood is floated down the narrow waterways into lakes. The mills situated on the banks of these lakes vary in size according to the amount of timber available for conversion.

The size of the logs available has influenced the development of mechanisation. In northern Europe the average softwood log is 300 to 450 mm in diameter, and the Swedish rack saw has over many years proved itself ideal for converting logs of this size. In North America the softwood logs are much larger, and the saws used are mainly circular and band saws which are capable of handling logs of large diameter.

Page 191 (top) shows the conversion of European redwood logs into deals and boards.

NOTE   The maximum section for deals is 100 × 250 mm. Large logs produce the best quality timber.

Page 191 (second) shows the section of a Columbian pine log. Notice the large area of first quality (prime) timber. The second quality timber is situated in the centre and outer area of the log. The timber in the centre contains numerous small knots, and the outer area timber includes the sapwood.

Page 191 shows, third, a method of sawing extensively used for all classes of timber. It is called through and through cutting or slab cutting. Only about 30% of the timber produced like this is suitable for high-class hardwood joinery.

Page 191 (foot) shows a way of sawing hardwood, especially oak, in order to produce the maximum quantity of good quality timber and the minimum of a poor quality. The method is a combination of quarter sawing and slab cutting.

NOTE   The heart is removed by slab cutting. Notice too the first quality timber obtained by quarter sawing.

Shrinkage and expansion of timber

The sapwood (the outer annual rings) of a tree contains more moisture than the heart wood. This results in unequal shrinkage during the drying (seasoning) process, which in its turn causes the wood to warp and twist. Page 192(1). shows the effect of unequal shrinkage on a slab-sawn log. The boards shrink away from the heart. The only straight boards are the rift or quarter sawn boards in the centre. Page 192 (2) shows the effect of unequal shrinkage on a log. Star shapes start from the outer rings. Page 192 (3) shows rectangular sections cut from the log. One may see the alteration in shape and size of the square section and the shrinkage away from the heart on the board section.

Page 192 (4) illustrates the three sections of a log:

(a)   The transverse or cross-section showing the annual ring and rays.

(b)   The radial section starting from the heart or centre of the log.

(c)   The tangential section at right angles to the radial section.

Any alteration in moisture content will bring about a change in size and shape. Timber expands or contracts very little in its length; therefore, provided the grain is straight, no bending or bowing will take place. The shrinkage on the tangential section is approximately twice that on the radial section. This accounts for the warping and twisting.

Seasoning

All freshly sawn timber contains a high percentage of moisture. This high moisture content must be reduced to suit the conditions under which the timber is to be used. A suitable moisture content for high-class joinery and cabinet work would be 5% to 10%, for general joinery work 7% to 15%, and for structural work, 15% to 20%. The moisture content can be calculated thus:

Wet weight − dry weight = weight of water (moisture content)

To determine the percentage of moisture content a small test piece is cut from the sample of wood before it is seasoned. In order to obtain a representative figure, this specimen should be cut at least 300 mm from one end of the sample board. Its length need not exceed 12 mm in the direction of the grain. The test piece should be weighed immediately, and this recorded as the *wet weight*. The specimen is next placed in an oven to withdraw the whole of the moisture, weighed again, and recorded as the *dry weight*.

$$\text{Percentage of moisture content} = \frac{\text{Wet weight} - \text{dry weight} \times 100}{\text{Dry weight}}$$

To take a simple example, suppose a specimen of a 25 mm board 12 mm long weighs 40 g before being seasoned (wet weight), and 30 g after it has been dried in an oven until the whole of the moisture has been withdrawn:

$$\text{MC} = \frac{40 - 30}{30} \times 100 = 33 \cdot 33 \text{ per cent}$$

Seasoning may be done in two distinct ways—naturally or by kiln. The main advantage of kiln seasoning is the measure of control it gives, so that each parcel or stack of timber can be reduced to the same moisture content. The time required for the process depends on the size of the timber—it usually takes between two and four days. The time required for air seasoning again depends on the size of the sections. Large sections may require six to twelve months, and small sections three to six months. If air seasoning could be carried out in buildings with the same air moisture content as the workshops, timber could generally be brought to a satisfactory moisture content in three to six months. It is usually accepted in the trade that timber which has been seasoned slowly will work more easily than that which has been seasoned quickly. Much progress has been made, however, in controlled methods of seasoning; techniques have been developed in this field which do not impair the quality of the wood.

Stacking is done in the same way for both air and kiln seasoning. The sawn timber must be carefully piled and stacked—usually at intervals of 900 to 1,200 mm—giving a free passage of air round each piece of timber. If stacked in the open air, the stacks are often provided with temporary cover.

Page 193 (top) shows the method for stacking round timber.

NOTE   The sticks are carefully placed over each other.

Page 193 (middle) shows the method for stacking deals. Page 193 (foot) shows the timber piled carefully on a platform or stand inside the kiln.

Building timbers in common use

SOFTWOODS	USES
European redwood (*Pinus sylvestris*)	General joinery
	Floor timbers
Columbian pine (*Pseudotsuga taxifolia*)	Roof timbers
	Floor coverings
Western red cedar (*Thuga plecata*)	Panelling
	Roof coverings
	(shingles)
Pitch pine (*Pinus palustris*)	Panelling
	Roof timbers
	Good class joinery
HARDWOODS	
Oak (*Quercus pedunculata*)	Panelling
	External joinery
	Church fittings
	Roof timbers

Teak (*Tectona grandis*)   High-class joinery
                                         Ship joinery
                                         Laboratory fittings
Mahogany (*Swietenia mahogoni*)   Panelling
                                         Cabinet joinery
Beech (*Fagius sylvatica*)   Floor coverings
                                         Furniture
                                         Woodworking planes

Manufactured boards

The manufactured boards used in the woodworking and building
industries include plywoods, fibre boards, chip boards and straw
boards.

Plywoods consist of thin layers of laminate with the grain alternatively across and lengthwise, glued together to form a strong
board which will retain its shape. Plywood is manufactured in
thicknesses varying from 3 to 40 mm.

Blockboards, which contain sawn strip cores, are also used in
large quantities. The structural form of plywoods and blockboards
is illustrated on page 194.

Fibre boards include insulating boards and hardboard, and were
first made in Sweden over thirty-five years ago.

Insulating boards (page 194—foot) can be got in thicknesses
varying from 6 to 24 mm. Hardboard manufacture has reached a
very high standard of efficiency, especially in Sweden. Boards have
been developed to suit many different purposes. They are extremely durable, and can be used with safety for any outside job.
Three thicknesses of boards are made—2 mm, 3 mm and 5 mm;
and these are produced in three grades—semi-hard, hard and
super-hard. In addition to the standard boards, many special
types are made, such as *peg boards* and *reeded boards*.

Details of the types of hardboards are given on page 195 (top).

The manufacture of *chip boards* (page 195—middle) is a post-
war development. The standard boards are 12 mm to 24 mm
thick, and large quantities of them are now being used in the
building and furniture industries.

Straw boards were first made in Sweden in 1936, and were
produced in Great Britain soon after the Second World War. The

boards are made of compressed straw 50 mm thick, covered by a waterproof paper skin which is sealed at all corners. Straw boards have excellent insulating qualities, and are used extensively for wall linings, ceilings, partitions and roof coverings (see page 195— foot).

Practice lessons

1 Working from the information given:

   (a) Make neat diagrams to show the growth structure of *hardwoods* and *softwoods*.

   (b) Show clearly the heart and sapwood areas.

2 *(a)* Make neat sketches to show how European softwood is converted into deals and boards.

   (b) Explain the following terms.
   (i) Through and through sawing.
   (ii) Quarter sawing.

3 *(a)* Make neat diagrams to illustrate the effects of shrinkage and expansion on timber.

   (b) Explain briefly the following technical terms:
   (i) Moisture content.
   (ii) Air seasoning.
   (iii) Kiln seasoning.

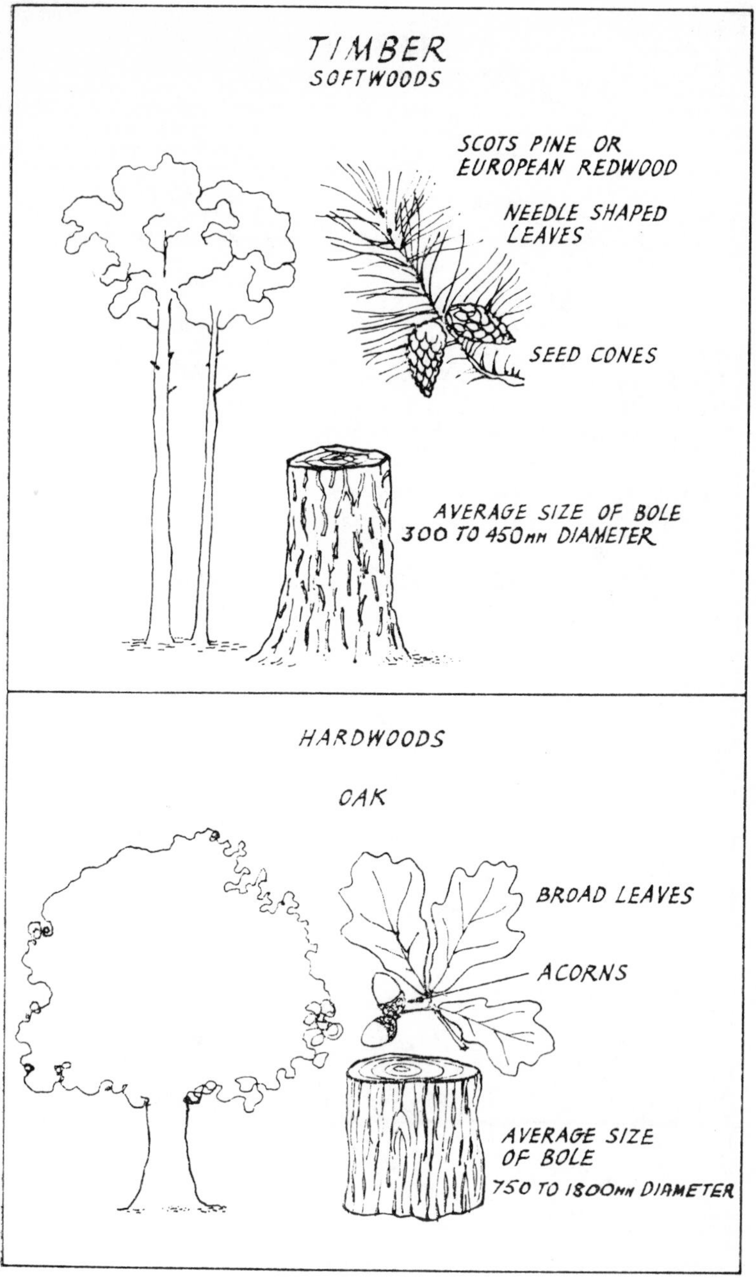

TIMBER
SOFTWOODS

SCOTS PINE OR
EUROPEAN REDWOOD

NEEDLE SHAPED
LEAVES

SEED CONES

AVERAGE SIZE OF BOLE
300 TO 450mm DIAMETER

HARDWOODS

OAK

BROAD LEAVES

ACORNS

AVERAGE SIZE
OF BOLE
750 TO 1800mm DIAMETER

189

TIMBER
THE STRUCTURE OF SOFTWOODS

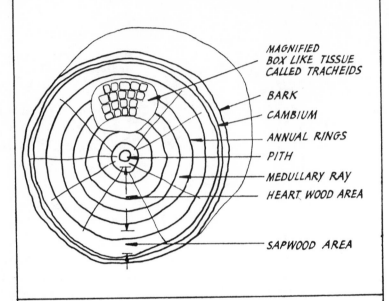

MAGNIFIED
BOX LIKE TISSUE
CALLED TRACHEIDS

BARK

CAMBIUM

ANNUAL RINGS

PITH

MEDULLARY RAY

HEART WOOD AREA

SAPWOOD AREA

THE STRUCTURE OF HARDWOODS

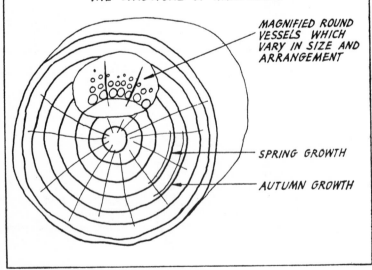

MAGNIFIED ROUND
VESSELS WHICH
VARY IN SIZE AND
ARRANGEMENT

SPRING GROWTH

AUTUMN GROWTH

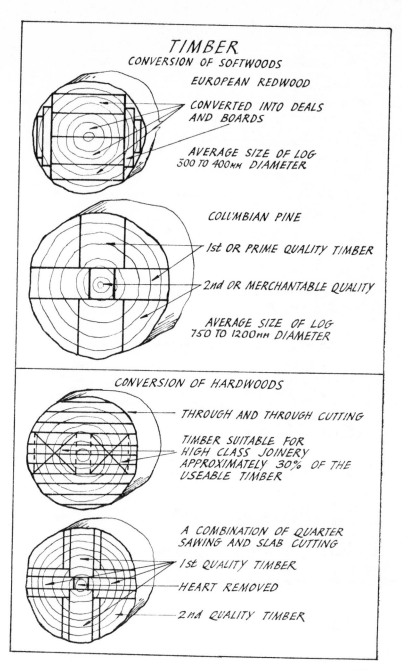

TIMBER

CONVERSION OF SOFTWOODS

EUROPEAN REDWOOD

CONVERTED INTO DEALS
AND BOARDS

AVERAGE SIZE OF LOG
300 TO 400mm DIAMETER

COLUMBIAN PINE

1st OR PRIME QUALITY TIMBER

2nd OR MERCHANTABLE QUALITY

AVERAGE SIZE OF LOG
750 TO 1200mm DIAMETER

CONVERSION OF HARDWOODS

THROUGH AND THROUGH CUTTING

TIMBER SUITABLE FOR
HIGH CLASS JOINERY
APPROXIMATELY 30% OF THE
USEABLE TIMBER

A COMBINATION OF QUARTER
SAWING AND SLAB CUTTING

1st QUALITY TIMBER

HEART REMOVED

2nd QUALITY TIMBER

TIMBER

SHRINKAGE AND EXPANSION OF TIMBER

UNEQUAL SHRINKAGE
ON A SLAB SAWN LOG

NOTE TIMBER SHRINKAGE
AWAY FROM THE HEART

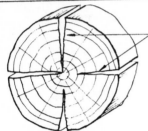

STAR SHAKE CAUSED BY
UNEQUAL SHRINKAGE

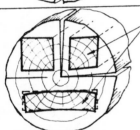

THE ALTERATION IN SIZE & SHAPE
OF RECTANGULAR SECTIONS
DUE TO UNEQUAL SHRINKAGE

NOTE THE SMALLER AND
DISTORTED SQUARE SECTIONS

THE AMOUNT OF UNEQUAL SHRINKAGE

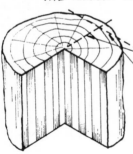

TIMBER SHRINKS VERY LITTLE
IN THE LENGTH

RADIAL SECTION

TANGENTIAL SECTION

NOTE THE SHRINKAGE ON THE
TANGENTIAL SECTION IS NEARLY
TWICE THAT OF THE RADIAL SECTION

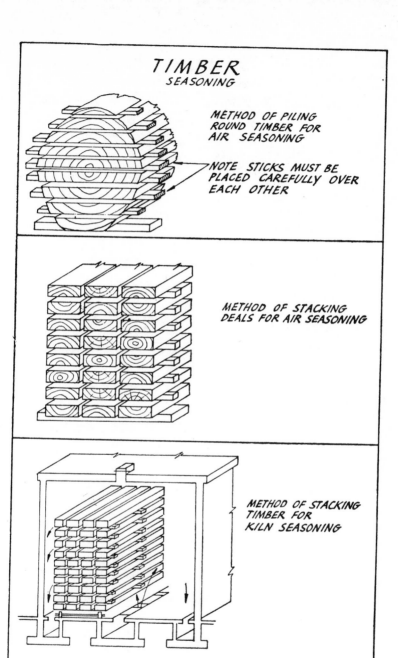

TIMBER
SEASONING

METHOD OF PILING
ROUND TIMBER FOR
AIR SEASONING

NOTE STICKS MUST BE
PLACED CAREFULLY OVER
EACH OTHER

METHOD OF STACKING
DEALS FOR AIR SEASONING

METHOD OF STACKING
TIMBER FOR
KILN SEASONING

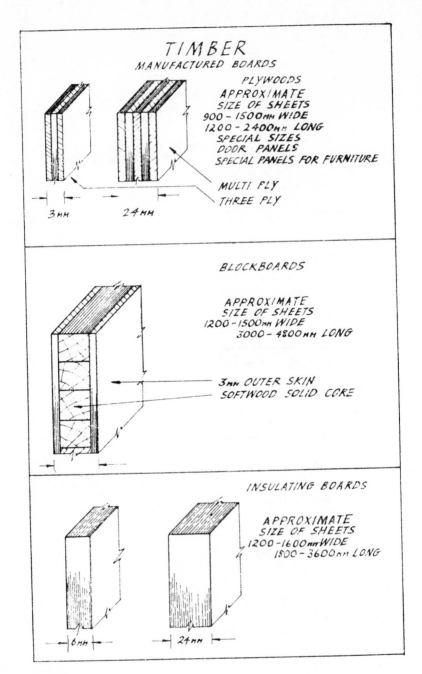

TIMBER
MANUFACTURED BOARDS

PLYWOODS
APPROXIMATE
SIZE OF SHEETS
900 - 1500mm WIDE
1200 - 2400mm LONG
SPECIAL SIZES
DOOR PANELS
SPECIAL PANELS FOR FURNITURE

MULTI PLY
THREE PLY

3mm   24mm

BLOCKBOARDS

APPROXIMATE
SIZE OF SHEETS
1200 - 1500mm WIDE
3000 - 4800mm LONG

3mm OUTER SKIN
SOFTWOOD SOLID CORE

INSULATING BOARDS

APPROXIMATE
SIZE OF SHEETS
1200 - 1600mm WIDE
1800 - 3600mm LONG

6mm   24mm

194

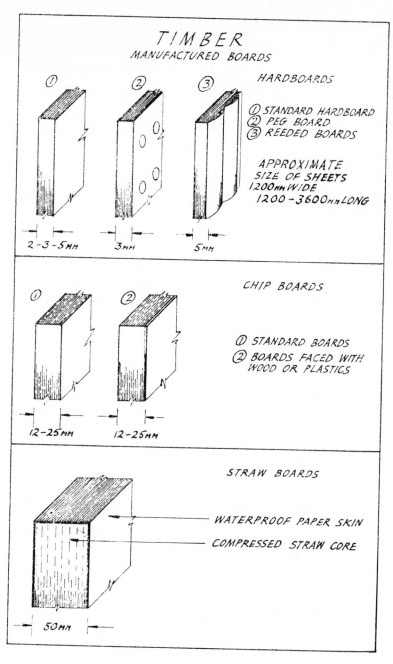

TIMBER
MANUFACTURED BOARDS

HARDBOARDS

① STANDARD HARDBOARD
② PEG BOARD
③ REEDED BOARDS

APPROXIMATE
SIZE OF SHEETS
1200mm WIDE
1200-3600mm LONG

2-3-5mm

3mm

5mm

CHIP BOARDS

① STANDARD BOARDS
② BOARDS FACED WITH WOOD OR PLASTICS

12-25mm

12-25mm

STRAW BOARDS

WATERPROOF PAPER SKIN

COMPRESSED STRAW CORE

50mm

Ironmongery used in carpentry and joinery is best classified as follows:

1 Metal fixings that penetrate the timber (nails, screws, coach screws, nuts and bolts).

2 Metal fixings that allow movement (hinges, pivots and so on).

3 Metal fixings that provide security (locks, draw bolts, casement fasteners and stays).

See pages 200–203.

Metal fixings that penetrate the timber

The many kinds of *nails* used are shown on page 200. *Round wire*, *oval* and *cut nails* are obtainable in lengths from 30 to 150 mm; *floor brads* in lengths of 56, 63 and 75 mm; and *panel pins* in lengths from 12 to 25 mm. *Clout nails* are used mainly for fixing felts and are obtainable in lengths from 12 to 25 mm.

The four main types of *screw* produced are illustrated on page 200. Screws may be obtained in many lengths—from 6 to 18 mm, rising in 3mm; from 18 to 63 mm, rising in 6mm; and from 63 to 150 mm, rising in 12 mm. The thickness of the screw's shank is denoted by a number—for example, 25 mm—8, 9 or 10. A number 14 screw is nearly 6 mm thick. Screws are made from mild steel and brass, and are obtainable in various enamelled and plated finishes.

The various kinds of *bolts* in use are given on page 200. *Nuts* and *bolts* are used mainly for bolting structures together; *coach screws* and *lewis bolts* are designed for securing machinery and so on to a floor or wall. Standard nuts and bolts are obtainable in lengths of 25 to 300 mm, and diameters of 6 mm to 40 mm.

Metal fixings that allow movement

Three main types of *hinges* are in general use—tee hinges, hooks and bands, and butt hinges (see illustrations on page 201).

Page 201 (top) gives details of a *tee hinge* and the method of fixing it. This hinge is used mainly on ledged and braced doors, and is obtainable in lengths from 100 to 600 mm.

Page 201 (middle) gives details of a pair of *hooks and bands*. The hooks may be 'screw on', 'drive in' or 'built in'. Used mainly on gates and garage doors, they are obtainable in lengths from 200 to 900 mm.

Butt hinges are used extensively for all classes of joinery and cabinet work. Page 201 (foot) gives details of a typical butt hinge, together with enlarged views showing the position of the two hinges on a flush door.

NOTE   The position of the lower hinge is arranged to give extra clearance between the door and floor, when the door is open at right angles.

Metal fixings that provide security

Three standard types of *lock* are in common use (see page 202). Rim locks and cylinder locks are usually fitted to external doors, and mortise locks to internal doors.

A *rim lock* consists of a lock body, a staple, a set of knobs or handles (called furniture), and an escutcheon plate. Page 202 (top) shows a rim lock fitted to a four-panelled door, with enlarged views of the lock, staple and furniture.

Mortise locks consist of a stock, a face plate and a striking plate, one set of knobs or handles, and two escutcheon plates. Page 202 (middle) shows the lock fitted to a flush door with enlarged details giving the position of the face and striking plates.

Cylinder locks consist of a stock containing the latch, a cylinder containing the key mechanism, and a staple into which the latch shoots. Page 202 (foot) shows a lock fitted to an entrance door with enlarged details of lock, staple and cylinder.

NOTE   Fixing instructions are given by all makers of cylinder latches.

There are various other types of fasteners. It is common practice to fit *barrel bolts* to all external doors. They are obtainable in lengths from 75 to 300 mm, and the quality varies from a japanned to a plated finish. Page 203 (top) shows two bolts fitted to an entrance door, giving enlarged details of bolt and keeper.

Norfolk latches are usually fitted to doors in outbuildings. The latch consists of latch, carrier and catch, details of which are given on page 203 (middle).

Casement fasteners and stays are used in every side-hung casement which requires one fastener fixed to the stile and one stay fixed to the bottom rail. Details of the fastener and stay are given on page 203 (foot).

Hand of locks and fasteners

The hand of a lock is determined by the direction in which the bolt shoots when viewed from the inside face of the lock, or by the hand used to open the door from the inside. The three illustrations on page 202 are all of left hand locks. The casement fastener, shown on page 202 (foot), is also left hand.

Practice lessons

1 Working from the information given:

   (a) Explain briefly the three classifications of builders ironmongery.

   (b) Make neat sketches of:

      (i) A floor brad and an oval nail.

      (ii) A cup-squarenut and bolt.

      (iii) A coach screw.

2 *(a)* Make a neat sketch of a butt hinge and name the various parts.

   (b) Draw, to a 1:5 scale, a tee hinge suitable for a standard size ledged and braced door. State size clearly.

3 *(a)* Draw an isometric view of a fitted mortise lock and striking plate as shown on page 202 (middle).

   (b) Make a neat sketch of a barrel bolt, and show its position on the door.

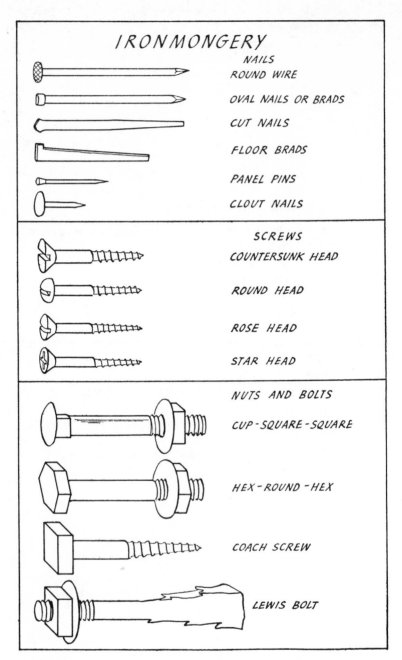

IRONMONGERY

NAILS

ROUND WIRE

OVAL NAILS OR BRADS

CUT NAILS

FLOOR BRADS

PANEL PINS

CLOUT NAILS

SCREWS

COUNTERSUNK HEAD

ROUND HEAD

ROSE HEAD

STAR HEAD

NUTS AND BOLTS

CUP - SQUARE - SQUARE

HEX - ROUND - HEX

COACH SCREW

LEWIS BOLT

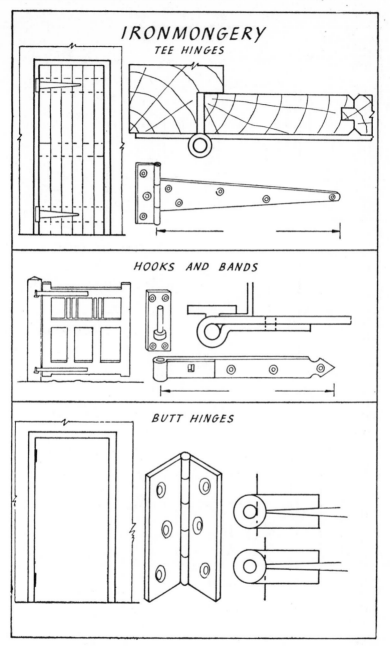

IRONMONGERY
TEE HINGES

HOOKS AND BANDS

BUTT HINGES

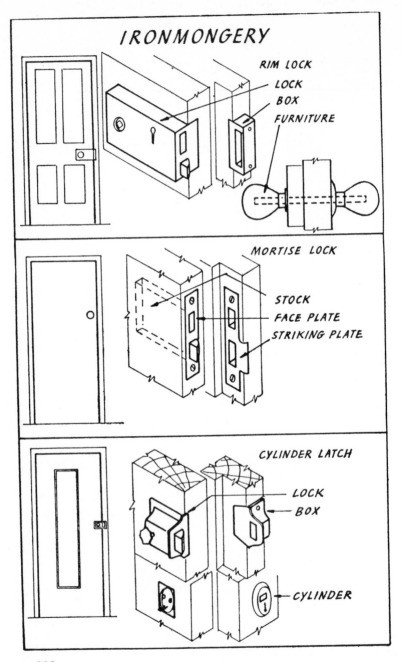

IRONMONGERY

RIM LOCK

LOCK
BOX
FURNITURE

MORTISE LOCK

STOCK
FACE PLATE
STRIKING PLATE

CYLINDER LATCH

LOCK
BOX

CYLINDER

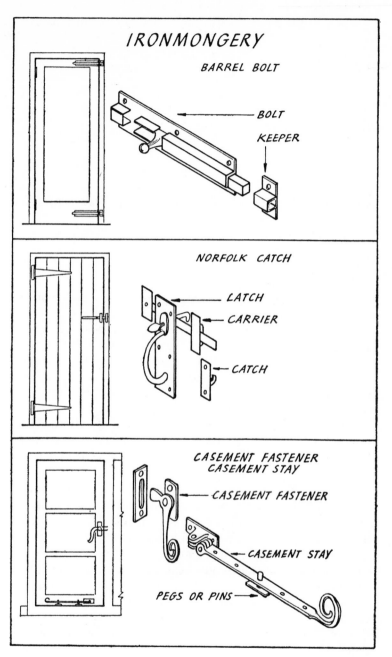

IRONMONGERY

BARREL BOLT

BOLT

KEEPER

NORFOLK CATCH

LATCH

CARRIER

CATCH

CASEMENT FASTENER
CASEMENT STAY

CASEMENT FASTENER

CASEMENT STAY

PEGS OR PINS

Four kinds of glue are in general use in the woodworking industries.
They are:

1   Animal glues.
2   Soya bean glues.
3   Casein glues.
4   Synthetic resins.

Animal glues are called hot glues. Bean, casein and synthetic
resins are cold glues.

Animal glues, or *hot glues*, need careful preparation. The glue is
sold in slab form, and must be broken up and soaked before being
heated. Glue pots and hot-water containers should be cleaned
frequently. The actual glueing-up operation must be done
speedily, and the glue must not be allowed to set until the joints
have been cramped together.

Bean glues, which are manufactured from Manchurian soya
beans are supplied in powder form and must be mixed with water.
These glues stain wood badly, and are not suitable for joinery or
cabinet work.

Casein glue is made from the solids in milk, is supplied in
powder form, and must be mixed with water. It is used extensively
in the manufacture of plywood, but its main disadvantage—that it
stains—makes it unsuitable for use in high-class joinery work.

The introduction of *resin glues* marked the beginning of a new
technique in the bonding, or glueing together of timber. Synthetic
resin glues are now universally used in all branches of carpentry
and joinery. Resin adhesives are waterproof, fungus proof and
very often stronger than many of the timbers that are bonded
together. To set the glue a chemical, called the hardener, is
needed.

Manufacturers give detailed instructions on the mixing and application of these glues.

Hints on glueing (see page 207)

1   Follow carefully the manufacturer's instructions when preparing the glue.

2   When glueing framed and panelled work, spread plenty of glue on the shoulders and haunchings.

3   On laminated work spread the glue evenly, and apply even pressure to all parts of the joint.

4   Snugly fitting joints are essential if maximum strength is required, since gap-filling glues can only take up at the most 1 mm.

Practice lessons

1 From the information given:

   (a) Name, and briefly describe, two adhesives that are in common use.

   (b) State briefly the purpose for which each is used, and how they are prepared for use.

2 *(a)* Make neat diagrams to show the application of the glue to the joint surface.

   (b) Explain why the shoulder area and the points of the wedges only are glued on framed joinery work.

ADHESIVES
APPLICATION

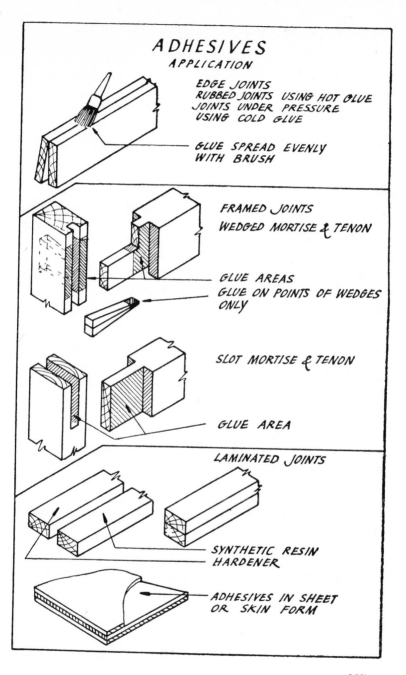

EDGE JOINTS
RUBBED JOINTS USING HOT GLUE
JOINTS UNDER PRESSURE
USING COLD GLUE

— GLUE SPREAD EVENLY
WITH BRUSH

FRAMED JOINTS

WEDGED MORTISE & TENON

GLUE AREAS
GLUE ON POINTS OF WEDGES
ONLY

SLOT MORTISE & TENON

GLUE AREA

LAMINATED JOINTS

SYNTHETIC RESIN
HARDENER

ADHESIVES IN SHEET
OR SKIN FORM

It is a mistake to think that workshop geometry and calculations are the concern only of the shop foreman or setter out. All measuring and calculating necessary to the carrying out of creative work can be considered as geometry and calculations, and everybody should take an interest in them. The instruments used include pencils, marking knives, rules, straight edges, try squares, set squares, bevels and compasses.

Measuring and marking

The lines indicating shoulders or distances should be as fine as is practicable. One should try to get cut lines to between 0·2 mm and 0·3 mm in thickness. A fine pencil line is about 0·3 mm in thickness.

The way to use *marking knives* and *pencils* is shown on page 216 (top). A fine line cut is made with the marking knife, and a fine line drawn with a chisel pointed pencil, since the usual pointed pencil will only retain its sharp point for a short time. A firm, hard pencil should be used; the grades most suitable are F, H and 3H.

Four fold *rules*, 1 m or 2 metres long, are extensively used, as shown on page 216 (foot).

NOTE The rule is placed on edge for marking small distances accurately. One rule is used for measuring distances of more than 2 metres and two rules are placed end to end to make possible the accurate measurement of long distances.

The proper use of a *scale rule* is not difficult to understand if one ignores the standard measure of 1 metre or 1 mm. Once the scale is selected that measurement is used as if it were a metre or mm.

The standard scales used in architecture and building are as follows:

1:200 and 1:100 and 1:50 for drawings of complete buildings
1:20 for details of sections of buildings
1:5 and full size for the sections of members.

Page 217 (top) shows the 1:100 scale on a rule.

The method of taking the dimensions from the drawings is also shown on page 217 (top). Three scales are illustrated underneath— the 1:100, 1:50 and 1:20. It will be noted that the scales only differ in size. The 1:50 scale is twice the size of the 1:100 scale, and the 1:20 five times the size of the 1:100 scale.

Division of lines and the spacing of members

Workshop methods of spacing out members and divisions of boards are illustrated on page 218.

Page 218 (top) shows a method of dividing a board into any number of equal parts. The five spaces on the rule are 40 mm each, making 200 mm from edge to edge.

Page 218 (below) shows the workshop methods for spacing out window members. In the first example single lines only are required.

NOTE In order to obtain the clear distance between each member, the intermediate members are pushed to one end.

In the second example one mullion is required, in the third three, and in the fourth two. The method of marking out the mortises for the bars is also shown in the fourth example.

The setting out of right angles

Every setting out job involves the drawing of right angles. Page 219 (top) shows a method of bisecting 180° to form a right angle.

The second drawing shows a method, using a try square and straight edge, which is much employed in the workshop.

The third drawing shows the application of the theorem of Pythagoras commonly known as the 3–4–5 method. This theorem is further dealt with on page 220 (top).

Page 219 (foot) shows a method for bisecting acute and obtuse angles.

The setting out of segmental curves

The data necessary for the drawing of segmental curves is the size of the rise and span. The radius can be found either by calculation or by drawing. Page 220 shows methods of doing this work by drawing. First, the angles AC and BC are bisected to obtain the centre O. Second, set squares are used for the same purpose.

Curves of small rise are best set out with the aid of a triangular frame or a board with the top edge shaped to the triangle ABC, as shown on page 220 (foot). Their radius lengths, since they are very long, make the use of a radius rod impracticable. One leg of the frame or board must be twice its own length to allow for the movement of the frame on the pins A and B.

NOTE   Semi-circular curves have a radius length of half the span, the centre being on the spring line.

Elliptical curves

If a cylinder is cut by an inclined plane the resulting shape is an ellipse. The projection of the true shape is shown on page 221 (top).

Below is shown the setting out of an elliptical-headed door frame by the cord and pin method. To find the position of the pins make the length from the pin crown to the crown focal points of the arch equal to half the span. A normal and tangent to the curve is also shown on the drawing. The normal will be the joint line.

Page 221 (foot) shows the short trammel method. The points on the trammel bar are found by taking half the length of the major axis, then, starting from the end, marking half the minor axis length on it. This gives the position of the two trammel heads.

Splayed work

The geometrical solid upon which splayed work is built is the pyramid. In order to find the true shape and bevels, each surface must be developed. Three typical examples of splayed work are given on page 222:

1 A splayed stall board
2 A splayed lining
3 A splayed hopper.

NOTE It is necessary to take a right angle view of the member in order to see its true shape.

The geometry of roofing

The geometry of roofing can best be understood from models. A right angle view must be taken of each member in order to see its true shape and size. If a study is made in this way full use can be made of the aids to roofing, and especially of the steel square.

Page 223 (top) is an isometric view of a hipped roof, showing the common rafters, hip rafters and jack rafters in position.

Page 223 (middle) shows the plan of the roof and the development of the common, hip, and jack rafters.

Page 223 (foot) shows the method which in practice is most popular.

NOTE All the members are projected from the base line.

Raking mouldings

When raking and level mouldings intersect at an angle, the shape of one section must be projected from the known section. A typical example of raking mouldings is shown on page 224 (top). A pitched dado rail intersects with level rails, and a pitched moulded string intersects a level skirting.

Page 224 (middle) shows the method of projecting the true shape of the level dado rails.

Page 224 (foot) shows the true shape of the level skirting.

Workshop calculations

The amounts of labour and material to be used on a job constitute the major part of workshop calculations.

Measuring in the length is called *lineal measure*.

Measuring in length and breadth gives area and is called *square measure*.

Measuring in length, breadth and thickness gives volume and is called *cube measure*.

Page 225 (top) illustrates measuring in the length, which is often called run measure.

Page 225 (middle) illustrates the square measure.

Page 225 (foot) illustrates the cube measure.

Measurement of timber

The change from imperial to metric measure means that the metre replaces the foot in length, the square metre replaces the square foot, and the cubic metre replaces the cubic foot.

The section sizes of timber are given in millimetres and the lengths in metres.

The diagram on page 226 represents a cubic metre of timber. It will be seen that a 300 mm cube is approximately equal to 1 cubic foot, and a 25 mm cube is approximately equal to 1 cubic inch.

Notice that the 300 mm or 1 cubic foot contains twelve boards 25 mm, or 1 inch, thick, and 144 feet of 1 in × 1 in. The cubic metre contains forty boards 25 mm thick and 1,600 metres of 25 × 25 mm.

The diagram at the foot of page 226 gives the section sizes of softwood relative to a cubic metre.

The charts give the lineal measurement of each section in metres.

The change from imperial to metric measure may mean that tongued and grooved boards will be measured in square metres and not in *squares*, the common trade practice. A square is an area 10 ft × 10 ft, that is 100 square feet. The nearest metric equivalent to 10 ft is 3 metres and 3^2 equals 9 square metres—in imperial measure 96·87 square feet—a reduction in area of say 3%.

The length of board required to cover one square metre will vary according to the width of the board.

Four standard widths of boards are shown:

1   150 mm wide boards will require 6·660 metres.
2   100 mm wide boards will require 10·000 metres.
3   125 mm wide boards will require 8·000 metres.
4   115 mm wide boards will require 8·700 metres.

The true volume of timber in a log could be found by taking the average sectional area and multiplying it by length, if all the timber were usable. However, this is not so in practice. The amount of usable timber is contained in a square, each side measuring one quarter of the average girth. The quarter girth formula, known as the Hoppus measure, may be expressed as follows:

$$\text{Volume in cubic metres} = \frac{\left(\dfrac{\text{girth in decimetres}}{4}\right)^2 \times \text{length in metres}}{100}$$

Page 228 (top) shows a log with 6 dm quarter girth, and a length of 4·3 m.

$$\text{Vol.} = \frac{\left(\dfrac{6 \times 4}{4}\right)^2 \times 4\cdot 3}{100}$$

= 1·548 cubic metres

Page 228 (foot) shows the amount of usable timber contained in the square and the four segments of waste.

The theorem of Pythagoras

This theorem has many applications in building calculations. By means of it, the lengths of roof timbers and the lengths of radii can be quickly obtained, and thus time can be saved in setting out.

Page 229 (top) shows the proof of the theorem.
Page 229 (middle) shows its application to roofing.
Page 229 (foot) shows its application to centring and arches.

The circle

One of the geometric truths relating to the circle is given on page 230 (top). Its application to carpentry and joinery is usually in connexion with radius lengths. Page 230 (middle) shows its application to joinery work and page 230 (foot) its application to carpentry work.

Practice lessons

1 Working from the information given on page 218, make dimensional sketches to show:

    (a)   The division of a board 265 mm wide into six equal parts.

    (b)   The spacing out of joinery members.

2 *(a)*   Explain the theory of Pythagoras and show its application to the setting out of right angles.

    (b)   Show two ways of setting out a segmental curve.

3 *(a)*   Show two ways of setting out an elliptical arch.

    (b)   Show on one drawing a normal and a tangent to the curve.

4 *(a)*   Draw the plan, section, and elevation view of the splayed lining illustrated on page 222. Scale 1 : 5.

    (b)   Project the true shape of the head and jamb lining.

5 *(a)*   Draw the plan of the hipped roof as illustrated on page 223. Span 6,000 m—Pitch 30°. Scale 1 : 50.

    (b)   Show, on the drawing, the length and side bevels of the common rafters and the hip rafter.

6 Working from the information given on page 224, project the true shape of the level dado rails marked A and B. Dado rail section 63 × 40 mm. Scale full size.

7 Working from the information given on page 229, determine the common rafter length of a roof when the span is 5.000 m and the rise 1.500 m.

8   Working from the information given on page 230:

  (a)   When AB equals 12 and C equals 3, calculate the radius
        length R.

  (b)   Apply the theorem of intersecting chords to determine
        the radius length for a large centre. Span 8.000 m. Rise
        1.500 m.

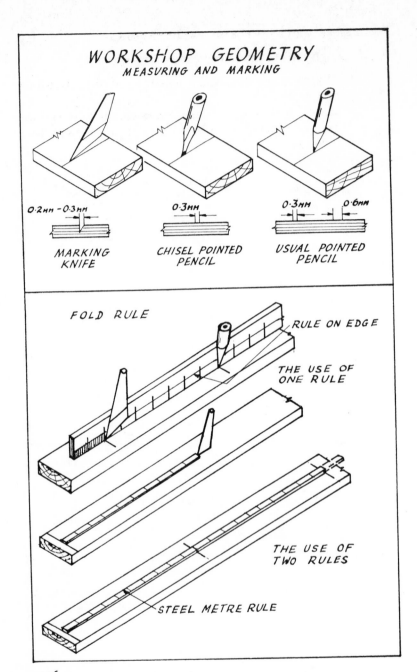

WORKSHOP GEOMETRY
MEASURING AND MARKING

0.2мм – 0.3мм

MARKING
KNIFE

0.3мм

CHISEL POINTED
PENCIL

0.3мм 0.6мм

USUAL POINTED
PENCIL

FOLD RULE

RULE ON EDGE

THE USE OF
ONE RULE

THE USE OF
TWO RULES

STEEL METRE RULE

WORKSHOP GEOMETRY
SCALE RULES

1·M

740

600

1 M

1:100
1:10

METHOD OF
TAKING DIMENSIONS
FROM DRAWING

STANDARD SCALES

4·8 M

1:100   1M 2   3   4   5   6   7   8   9   10   1:100 SCALE

3·7 M

1:50   1M   2   3   4   5   1:50 SCALE

1·4 M

1:20   1M   2   1:20 SCALE

WORKSHOP GEOMETRY
DIVISION OF LINES AND SPACING OF MEMBERS.

DIVISION OF BOARD INTO
FIVE EQUAL SPACES

TWO LIGHT WINDOW HEAD

FOUR LIGHT
WINDOW HEAD

4 EQUAL SPACES

THREE LIGHT
WINDOW HEAD

NOTE MULLIONS PUSHED TO ONE END

WORKSHOP GEOMETRY
THE SETTING OUT OF RIGHTANGLES

METHOD OF BISECTING 180° TO FORM A RIGHTANGLE

THE USE OF SQUARE AND STRAIGHT EDGE

THE APPLICATION OF THEORY OF PYTHAGORAS

METHOD OF BISECTING ACUTE AND OBTUSE ANGLES

WORKSHOP GEOMETRY
THE SETTING OUT OF SEGMENTAL CURVES

THE BISECTING OF ANGLES A.C & B.C
TO OBTAIN CENTRE O

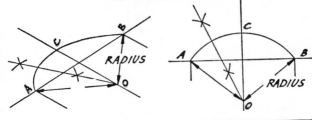

RADIUS

RADIUS

THE USE OF SET SQUARES TO OBTAIN CENTRE O

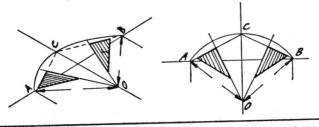

METHOD OF MARKING OUT CURVES OF SMALL RISE

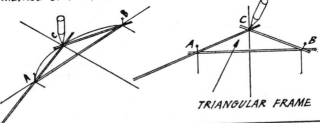

TRIANGULAR FRAME

METHOD OF MARKING OUT SMALL CURVES

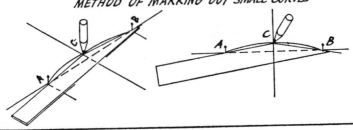

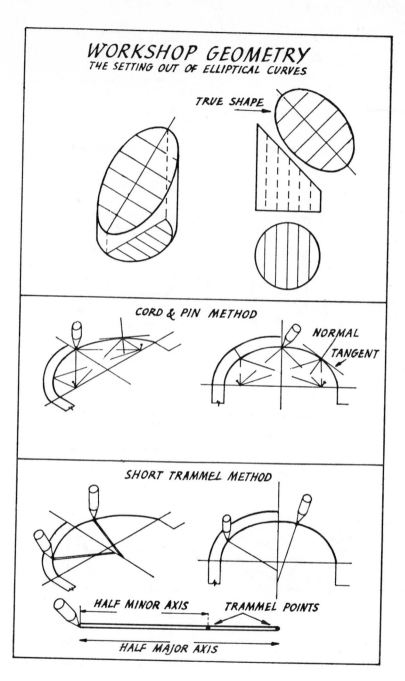

WORKSHOP GEOMETRY
THE SETTING OUT OF ELLIPTICAL CURVES

TRUE SHAPE

CORD & PIN METHOD

NORMAL

TANGENT

SHORT TRAMMEL METHOD

HALF MINOR AXIS

TRAMMEL POINTS

HALF MAJOR AXIS

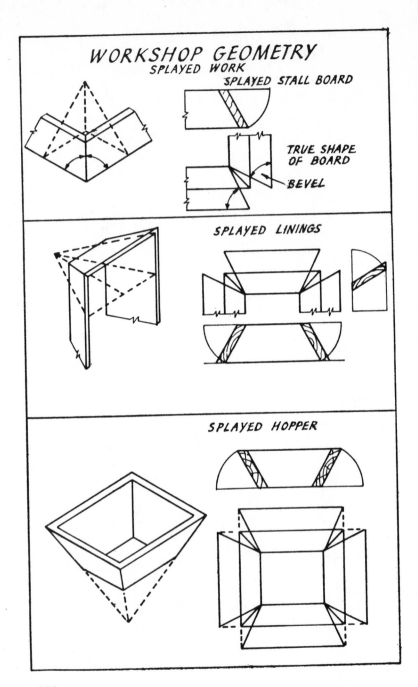

WORKSHOP GEOMETRY
SPLAYED WORK

SPLAYED STALL BOARD

TRUE SHAPE
OF BOARD

BEVEL

SPLAYED LININGS

SPLAYED HOPPER

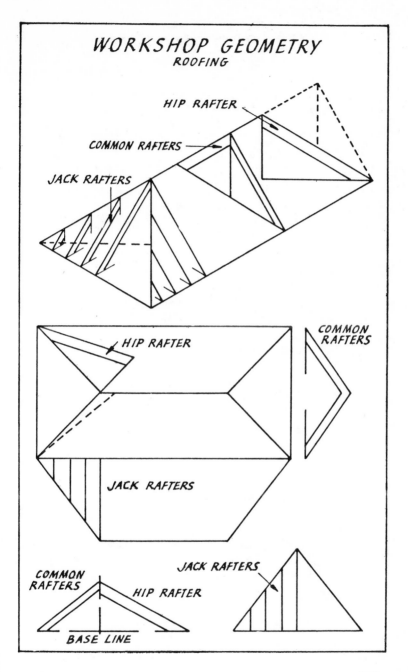

WORKSHOP GEOMETRY
ROOFING

HIP RAFTER

COMMON RAFTERS

JACK RAFTERS

HIP RAFTER

COMMON RAFTERS

JACK RAFTERS

COMMON RAFTERS

HIP RAFTER

BASE LINE

JACK RAFTERS

223

WORKSHOP GEOMETRY
RAKING MOULDINGS

DADO RAIL

STRING

DADO RAIL
SECTION

STRING SECTION

DADO RAIL

TRUE SHAPE OF
LEVEL DADO RAIL Ⓐ

TRUE SHAPE OF LEVEL
DADO RAIL Ⓑ

PLAN

SKIRTING AND STRING INTERSECTIONS

STRING SECTION

TRUE SHAPE OF LEVEL SKIRTING

WORKSHOP CALCULATIONS
LINEAL MEASURE

SQUARE MEASURE

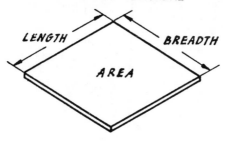

CUBE MEASURE

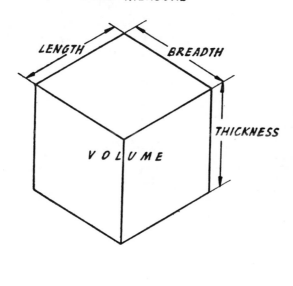

WORKSHOP CALCULATIONS
MEASUREMENT OF TIMBER

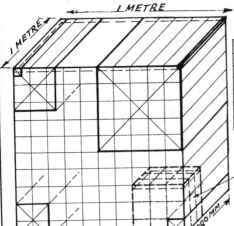

1 CUBIC METRE CONTAINS		
1	METRE	1000 × 1000
4	"	500 × 500
10	"	250 × 250
25	"	200 × 200
100	"	100 × 100
400	"	50 × 50
1600	"	25 × 25

A CUBE MEASURING
300 × 300 × 300 MM
IS APPROXIMATELY
EQUAL TO
ONE CUBIC FOOT

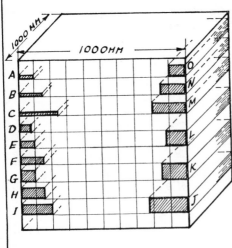

A	400 M	25 × 100
B	266·6 M	25 × 150
C	160 M	25 × 250
D	266·6 M	50 × 75
E	200 M	50 × 100
F	133·3 M	50 × 150
G	133·3 M	75 × 100
H	88·8 M	75 × 150
I	66·6 M	75 × 200
J	44·4 M	100 × 225
K	66·6 M	100 × 150
L	80 M	100 × 125
M	80 M	63 × 200
N	106·6 M	63 × 150
O	160 M	63 × 100

WORKSHOP CALCULATIONS
METHOD OF MEASURING TONGUED & GROOVED BOARD

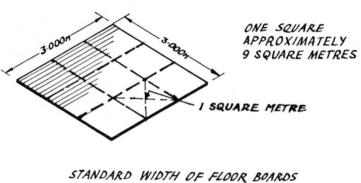

ONE SQUARE
APPROXIMATELY
9 SQUARE METRES

3.000M

3.000M

I SQUARE METRE

STANDARD WIDTH OF FLOOR BOARDS

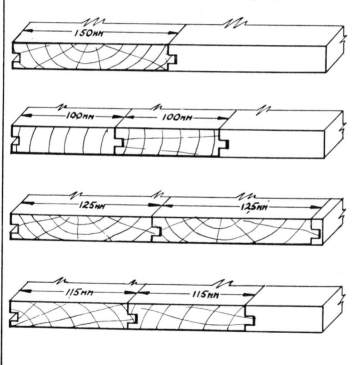

150MM

100MM — 100MM

125MM — 125MM

115MM — 115MM

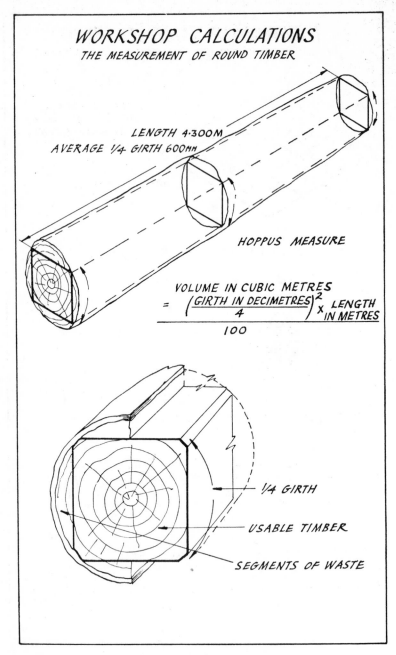

WORKSHOP CALCULATIONS
THE MEASUREMENT OF ROUND TIMBER

LENGTH 4·300M

AVERAGE 1/4 GIRTH 600mm

HOPPUS MEASURE

VOLUME IN CUBIC METRES

$$= \frac{\left(\dfrac{GIRTH\ IN\ DECIMETRES}{4}\right)^2 \times \dfrac{LENGTH}{IN\ METRES}}{100}$$

1/4 GIRTH

USABLE TIMBER

SEGMENTS OF WASTE

WORKSHOP CALCULATIONS

THEOREM OF PYTHAGORAS

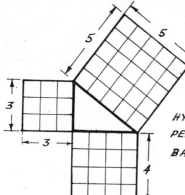

IN ANY RIGHT ANGLE TRIANGLE THE SQUARE ON THE HYPOTENUSE IS EQUAL TO THE SUM OF THE SQUARES ON THE SIDES CONTAINING THE RIGHT ANGLE

HYPOTENUSE	5×5	$= 25$
PERPENDICULAR	3×3	$= 9$
BASE	4×4	$= 16$

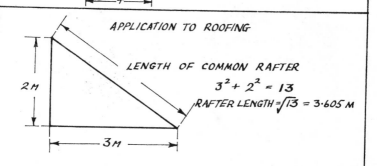

APPLICATION TO ROOFING

LENGTH OF COMMON RAFTER

$$3^2 + 2^2 = 13$$

RAFTER LENGTH $= \sqrt{13} = 3.605$ M

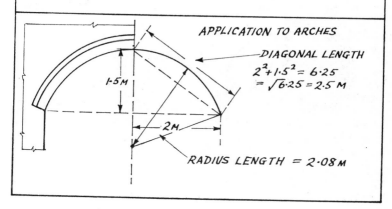

APPLICATION TO ARCHES

DIAGONAL LENGTH

$$2^2 + 1.5^2 = 6.25$$
$$= \sqrt{6.25} = 2.5 \text{ M}$$

RADIUS LENGTH $= 2.08$ M

WORKSHOP CALCULATIONS
THE CIRCLE

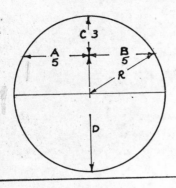

IF TWO CHORDS OF A CIRCLE INTERSECT THE PRODUCT OF THE TWO PARTS OF ONE CHORD IS EQUAL TO THE PRODUCT OF THE TWO PARTS OF THE OTHER CHORD

$$A \times B = C \times D$$
$$5 \times 5 = 3 \times D$$
$$D = \frac{25}{3} = 8.33$$

$$RADIUS = \frac{3 + 8.33}{2} = 5.66$$

APPLICATION TO JOINERY.

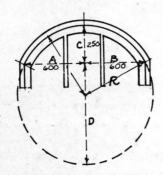

RADIUS LENGTH =
$$60 \times 60 = 25 \times D$$
$$D = \frac{360}{25} = 140.4$$
$$R = \frac{25 + 140.4}{2} = 8.27 \text{MM}$$

APPLICATION TO CARPENTRY

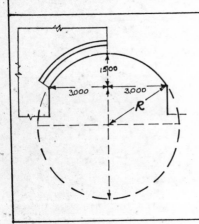

RADIUS LENGTH
$$30 \times 30 = 15 \times D$$
$$D \quad \frac{900}{15} = 60$$
$$R = \frac{15 + 60}{2} = 3.750 \text{M}$$